THE INSCRIPTIONAL WORK OF ERIC GILL

'. . . an inscription
bitten into the stones that guard our ashes, which can be broken
apart by the rude strength of a wild fig.'

From *Juvenal*, *10. 143–145*
(translated by GILBERT HIGHET)

EVAN R. GILL

THE
INSCRIPTIONAL WORK
OF ERIC GILL

AN INVENTORY

CASSELL & CO LTD · LONDON

CASSELL & CO LTD

35 Red Lion Square · London WC1

and at

MELBOURNE · SYDNEY · TORONTO

JOHANNESBURG · CAPE TOWN · AUCKLAND

©

EVAN R. GILL

1964

Printed in Great Britain
at The Curwen Press

F.064

CONTENTS

Account of Work Done for W. D. Caröe Esq.
from August 28 to September 9th 1901.

Description		Time		Hours
S. Michael Edmonton Foundation Stone	—	8.30 - 11.0	PM	2½
"	—	8.30 - 9.30	AM	1
Christchurch Clericks Foundation Stone	—	6.30 - 10.30	PM	4
"	—	8.30 - 9.30	AM	1
"	—	6.30 - 8.30	PM	2½
S. John Byfleet Protective	—	10.30 - 1.0	AM—PM	2½
"	—	6.50 - 7.50	AM	½
"	—	10.0 - 1.0	AM—PM	3
Edmonton Foundation Stone	—	6.0 - 8.0	PM	2
"	—	8.0 - 10.0	PM	2
"	—	4.30 - 5.30	PM	1 ¾
"	—	10.15 - 12.0	AM	1 ¾

23 ¾

£1 : 3 : 9 .

A.E.R. Gill

Account of Work Done for W. D. Caröe (reduced)

PREFACE

Lettering in history exhibits diverse forms and mediums. The attempt is here made to record the inscriptional work, whether incised into stone, painted upon wood or engraved in metal, by one of the most copious executants of the art known in our time: Eric Gill.

Let it be said at the outset that this record is not complete and, further, that the treatment of the entries is not uniform. This is inevitable for reasons which I shall try to make clear. Then too, what has been recorded was not always wholly the work of one man's hands. First let me speak of the questions of completeness and uniformity.

SOURCES

Though Eric Gill was in important respects the most methodical of men, his eye, more particularly at the outset of his career as a letter-cutter, was directed more closely to the job in hand rather than to its recording in a catalogue, for the benefit of himself or any other who should come after. Rather, the job itself was its own record. This is not to imply that he kept *no* records of work done. We have his personal diaries (kept most meticulously), one or two note-books and, most valuable of all an 'exercise' book entitled *List of Jobs*. This was begun in 1902 and carries us to the end of 1909.

Earlier than the diaries or the note-books, as sources of information for E.G.'s inscriptional work, are the two Statements of Account he rendered to W. D. Caröe, architect to the Ecclesiastical Commissioners, in whose drawing office he worked (somewhat unhappily) for the three years 1900–2. Both sources relate to work done for Caröe in 1901. They are of such paramount interest that it is worth while placing them on record. The earlier of the two (from his lodgings at 68 Victoria Road, Clapham) is for the following jobs:

	hrs.
Clapton—Foundation stone, June 21–25	8¾
Canterbury Chapel—Dedication stone, July 1–2	4½
,, ,, (revised) July 10	2
Trinity Lodge, Cambridge, July 16	2½
,, ,, & Cranbrook door, July 18–19	4¾
Total	22½

As his charges were based at the rate of 1s. per hour the bill amounted to £1. 2s. 6d.!

Let us now return to the *List of Jobs*. This, unfortunately, with very few exceptions, proved of limited value in supplying us with the kind of detailed information we desired for the Inventory. The name of the person or institution commemorated and the location of the work, are lacking. E.G. gives the number, name of client and a brief note of the work. That is all. An example will show what the record comprises.

122 Mr. Williams White. Memorial Tablet. Bognor.

Which being interpreted (cf. No. 66) means:

Memorial brass in St. Wilfred's Church, Bognor, in memory of James Allen Freeborn Howell, 1887–1904, a pupil at a school of which Williams White was the head-master.

It will now be appreciated why not every one of the inscriptional jobs is recorded here; and also why, for such as have been given, the entries are lacking in uniformity. For the rest—E.G.'s work done subsequent to 1909—the compiler has had to rely (with one major exception) almost wholly on the diary entries; themselves cryptic, sketchy or ambiguous. The reader must remember that the diary entries were solely for E.G.'s own information.

We now come to the major exception referred to above. By way of introduction let me outline the procedure E.G. generally followed when approached with a commission. It was his general practice to submit to his client either a sketch or a finished drawing of the proposed memorial. This, if approved, would be returned to him. He would then prepare a full-scale drawing. A considerable number, though, as will be seen, by no means all, of the original sketches or drawings would find their way back to his client. Fortunately for us, however, E.G. retained a great many of these. Still more fortunately the Monotype Corporation was able to acquire from the Executors of the estate this collection of sketches and drawings, together with a very considerable number of rubbings of the finished works. Without these 'pieces' the present work could hardly have been compiled. The following figures will serve to illustrate the point.

Our Catalogue lists some 808 entries of 'Jobs Done'. Of these there are no less than 635 sketches or drawings in the Monotype collection which represent 376 distinct works—roughly 46 per cent of the total. It should be noted that these figures do not take the rubbings into account.

The descriptions of these jobs in the catalogue, it need hardly be emphasized, are of necessity compressed into a few lines, without regard to size, purpose or importance. Let me illustrate my point by referring the reader to the War Memorial for New College (No. 398) which involved cutting no less than 270 2 in. and 5,060 1 in. capital letters! An extreme example, doubtless, but one which is not without significance.

ATTRIBUTION OF THE WORKS

An important question immediately poses itself. Is it possible to segregate the work of E.G.'s own hands, absolutely, from that of his assistants?[1] The answer must be 'No'. Nor would an attempt at such a segregation necessarily be desirable even if it were possible—for reasons which it is hoped to make convincing. No hard and fast line can be drawn between the inscriptions which came wholly and absolutely from his hands, or partly his and those of his assistants, or were interpreted either in whole or in part by one or more of his assistants. This aspect of his work as sculptor or letter-cutter and his attitude towards the principles involved was admirably treated by his very close friend the late Father Desmond Chute in a study of E.G.'s work as yet unpublished. I am grateful for permission to quote from it:

'On Ditchling Common, at Capel-y-ffin or wherever Gill set up shop, life was lived on this [a small workshop manned by a group no larger than a family] model in a passion of shared work and ideas. Work did not end where leisure began, for leisure was but another kind of work. Everything made there was wholly inspired and entirely due to him. This does not necessarily mean that all works came wholly from his hand. For if in a period when sculptors' use of the pointing machine was taken for granted, he was adamant against this or other devices that rob men of responsibility, on the other hand he made ample use of the collaboration of fellow stonecutters, esteeming this a mutual benefit. Nor did he hesitate to set his name to work thus produced—metaphorically in most cases, for he did not hold with signed work.

'Whereas then in one sense everything shown in this book is his, in another few are the works which owe nothing to his assistants, while fewer still proceed from the master's hand alone.[2] One or two (e.g. Nos. 330–1 and 342) are definitely *bottega* works cut wholly by apprentices or pupils. Their inclusion is deliberate as illustrating the workshop system itself and his conception of it, and because it is what Eric would have wished.

'To anyone who has learnt a craft in a workshop the elaborate *expertise* whose aim is to spot the master's hand, isolating his work from that of the school, is simply laughable. The touches of the master are as fleeting as they are frequent whereas the imprint of his mind is everywhere and not least in what he has least touched.

'At times someone would happen to single out an inscription and Eric would say "I'm glad you like that: Albert (or Laurie or Denis) cut it". He no more sought to conceal the fact than it would have occurred to him to show or sell the stone under the assistant's name, so long as he was such. In the workshop anonymity stands for distinction not privation. There was no

[1] Gill's first apprentice, Joseph Cribb, came to him in June 1906. All the works therefore from 1901 to that date may rightly be regarded as wholly the work of Gill's hands.
[2] The reader must be told that Fr. Chute's study was concerned primarily with sculptures.

shortage of outstanding masons in the Middle Ages: that is why they ceased to stand out. Besides, anonymity is more than namelessness, not just an historical accident but a peculiar positive quality. In Gill's own words, "If every single mediaeval carving were signed and not a single modern one, it would still be true that mediaeval art is 'anonymous' and modern art isn't''. But his was. And so was that of his pupils.'

As to Fr. Chute's reference to 'signed' work, so rarely did Eric 'sign' his work that it may be of interest to draw attention to three exceptions to his general rule. These are the Lawley monument in Escrick church (No. 96) erected in 1906, the large War Memorial for the staff of the V. & A. Museum, South Kensington (No. 365) erected in 1919 and the Hamersley tablet of 1930 at Rycote, near Thame (No. 542). The second of these carries, too, the 'signature' of Joseph Cribb who, happy to relate, after fifty-five years at the game is still carving a niche for himself and the craft of letter-cutting in Ditchling, whither he migrated in 1907 with his master from London.

Let me, please, here pay tribute in my personal capacity to all those 'chaps' (Eric's word for them) who so faithfully served him indoors and out of doors, in all weathers, in good times and bad, at some time or other between the years from 1906 to 1940 the year of his death. The least I can do is record their names as I have done in an Appendix to this catalogue.

It is necessary to add that as a matter of course Joseph Cribb and the other chaps who assisted in the execution of the inscriptional commissions that came into the workshop, were all masters of the letter forms which had earlier, under Eric Gill's sole hand evolved into that fully developed and perfected style which is his own individual and, it has been said by a competent judge, 'immortal' contribution to the lapidary art.

A record of this kind owes much to relatives of the persons commemorated, to incumbents of parishes and to officials of institutions with whom I have corresponded. Their replies have been uniformly helpful; several letters concerning memorials in church and public institutions have revealed a heart-warming interest and pleasure in learning, for the first time, who was responsible for the design and execution of the memorials in their care.

My correspondents are far too numerous to mention by name but I here express my gratitude to them and, in particular, to officials of two libraries in which I have worked—the Guildhall in London, and the Picton in Liverpool; also to the following whose help was very considerable—the late Mrs. Eric Gill, her daughter Mrs. René Hague, her son-in-law Mr. Denis Tegetmeier, my brother Major V. K. Gill, also Mr. David Peace, A.R.I.B.A., M.T.P.I., Mr. Stanley Scott, Mr. Walter Shewring and Mr. Roger Smith.

In conclusion I acknowledge my indebtedness to the Monotype Corporation for having facilitated my progress through the maze of material in Monotype House and for the assistance given me by various members of their staff, above all to Mr. John Dreyfus for the guidance and advice he gave me so frequently, patiently and ungrudgingly.

LIVERPOOL—1963   E.R.G.

LIST OF PLATES

APPRENTICES, PUPILS OR ASSISTANTS

(*Denotes Apprentices)

LONDON: 1906–8

CHRISTIE, Lawrence (1907–8)
*CRIBB, Herbert Joseph (1906–8)
GILL, Macdonald (1906–8)
STAPLETON, George (1906–7)

DITCHLING: 1907–24

BEEDHAM, Ralph J. (1917–24)
CHUTE, Desmond (1918–22)
CRIBB, Herbert Joseph (1907–24)
CRIBB, Laurence (1922–24)
*GEERING, S. (1914–15)
GILL, Macdonald (1907–24)
HAGREEN, Philip (1924–25)
JONES, David (1921–24)
*LEANEY, Albert (1914–21)
*STRATTON, Hilary (1920–21)
TEGETMEIER, Denis (1921)
TOMSETT, George (1914–20)
*WHITE, Frederick (1910–12)

CAPEL-Y-FFIN: 1924–28

ANSTED, René (1925–27)
CRIBB, Herbert Joseph (1924–28)
CRIBB, Laurence (1924–28)
JONES, David (1924–27)

PIGOTTS, HIGH WYCOMBE: 1928–40

BEYER, Ralph (1937–38)
CRIBB, Herbert Joseph (1928–34)
CRIBB, Laurence (1928–40)
FOSTER, Anthony (1933–40)
KINDERSLEY, David (1934–36)
LORIMER, Hew (1934–35)
MACDOUGALL, Angus (1934–36)
PELHAM, Prudence (1930–31)
POTTER, Donald (1931–32)
RICHEY, Michael (1936–39)
RITCHIE, Walter (1938–39)
SHARPE, John (1937)
*SKELTON, John (1940)
TEGETMEIER, Denis (1928–40)

Note: Eric Gill moved from London (Hammersmith) to Ditchling 12 September 1907 but retained a workshop at Hammersmith until 23 April 1908. The Capel-y-ffin period was from 13 August 1924 until 11 October 1928 when he moved to Pigotts. He died 17 November 1940.

THE INVENTORY
1900-1940

HEIGHT AND WIDTH are stated throughout in inches.

DIMENSIONS indicate the area of the complete work, inclusive of features such as coats of arms, foliage, or crucifix which may extend beyond the area of the inscription.

F.S. indicates full-size.

THE INVENTORY
1900-1940

1 Inscription on stone: JANE LISTER A DEAR CHILD. Eric Gill's first letter-cutting on stone doubtless inspired by the wall tablet in Westminster Abbey Cloisters, which reads 'IANE LISTER dear childe died Oct 7 1688'. Eric Gill's carving now in the possession of Mrs. René Hague at Pigotts, High Wycombe. Though unsigned this is inscribed on reverse 'My first inscpt'.
Size of carving: $7\frac{1}{2} \times 11\frac{1}{2}$; *c.* 1901.   [*See Plate I*]

2 Stone tablet in Chichester Cathedral in memory of PERCY JOSEPH HISCOCK, d. 1900.
Ink drawing of letters; $8\frac{1}{4} \times 19\frac{1}{4}$; signed A. E. R. Gill, 68 Victoria Road, Clapham, S.W.
The original drawing has the following pencilled note on reverse: 'A.E.R.G. 1901, before attending L.C.C. & before E. J[ohnston]'s teaching.'
Work executed 1901.

3 Foundation stone in cloister of Charterhouse School, Godalming, Surrey. August 1901.
(See also No. 12.)

4 Foundation stone for St. Michael, Edmonton. August 1901.

5 Inscription in memory of WILLIAM FRANCIS WILLIAMS, d. 1858, also of ROBERT HENRY WILLIAMS, d. 1864, and FANNY EMILY SORRELL, d. 1900.
Rubbing; $38 \times 25\frac{3}{4}$; [n.d.] *c.* 1901.

6 Tombstone in Brookwood Cemetery, Surrey, in memory of JOHN WINTERBOTHAM BATTEN, K.C.—1831–1901.
Cut in April 1902. A second inscription, in memory of SARAH LANG-STAFF BATTEN—1835–1908, was added in 1909.
Rubbing of first inscription; 18×23; 1902.
Rubbing of second inscription; $19\frac{3}{4} \times 27$; signed A. E. R. Gill.

7 Tombstone, with inscription in French, in memory of ALICE JUNOD, d. 7 March 1902.
Rubbing of inscription; 12 × 16½; signed, but undated, A. E. R. Gill, 16 Old Buildings, Lincoln's Inn, W.C. [May 1902.]

8 Inscription for choir seats, St. Paul, Carlton-in-the-Willows, Nottingham. January 1903.

9 The eighth Commandment: THOU SHALT NOT STEAL.
The letters (3¼ in. high), surmounted by a cross, incised and gilded on a board of stained oak screwed on to the panelling in the library at Madresfield Court, Malvern, Worcs., the Seat of Lord Beauchamp.
The inscription measures 44 × 9. July–August 1903. [One of E.G.'s earliest inscriptions. For the following notes the compiler is indebted to Mr. David Peace: 'Uprights are slightly widened towards the top—an interesting early quirk of originality. The serifs are mixed; the E & L are interestingly wide; but the whole thing hangs together very well.']
The work was commissioned by Graily Hewitt on behalf of William Lygon, 7th Earl Beachamp (1872–1938).

10 Tablet on outside wall and south of main door, Holy Trinity, Sloane Street, London, in memory of Admiral Sir GEORGE OMMANEY WILLES, G.C.B. 1823–1901. Recording the gift of gates and railings erected by his widow.
'Easter A.D. 1903.'
Rubbing; 19 × 20; July 1903.

11 Inscription on pediment in the Medical School, Downing Street, Cambridge. July 1903.
An additional inscription, diamond shaped, MEDICAL SCHOOL, was cut in November 1915.
Rubbing; 13½ × 25; signed Cambridge Nov. 1915, H.J.C.

12 A series of panels in the hall of Charterhouse School, Godalming, recording the names of scholars. Panels of various sizes, the smallest being 9 × 13⅝.
Full-size drawings endorsed by E.G.: 'A.E.R.G. for W. D. Caröe, 1903.'
(See also No. 3.)

13 Epitaph incised direct on the S.E. face of the chancel arch in St. Mary's, Burpham, Arundel, Sussex, in memory of FRANCIS JOHN MOUNT, Archdeacon of Chichester, b. 14th October 1831, d. 9th May 1903.

Pen and ink drawing; $16\frac{1}{4} \times 17$; signed A. E. R. Gill, 16 Old Buildings, Lincoln's Inn.

Work executed August 1903.   [*See Plate IV*]

14 Headstone for grave in St. Marylebone Cemetery, Finchley, London, in memory of EMILY ADELAIDE MAKINS, d. 13 June 1903.
Rubbing of inscription; $22 \times 16\frac{3}{4}$; August 1903.

15 War Memorial in Danejohn Park, Canterbury, for the 1st and 2nd Volunteer Battalions 'THE BUFFS' and ROYAL EAST KENT IMPERIAL YEOMANRY.
Full-size drawings 43×19, $39\frac{1}{2} \times 38\frac{1}{2}$, and 81×39; signed A. E. R. Gill, September 1903.
(See also No. 32.)

16 Painted letters on fascia and in the tea-room of bookshop for W. H. SMITH & SON, Rue de Rivoli, Paris.
Lettering (for fascia); $29\frac{3}{4} \times 21\frac{1}{2}$. September 1903.
[This was the first of several similar jobs Gill did for this firm which led to the adoption of the same style lettering for their bookshops and railway bookstalls throughout Great Britain.]

17 Incised inscriptions on three beams, each 10 feet in length, on lych gate of St. Mary's, Great Warley, Essex.
A. THIS LYCH GATE WAS ERECTED ANNO DOMINI MCMIII IN THE REIGN OF KING EDWARD VII.
B. TO GUIDE OUR FEET INTO THE WAY OF PEACE.
C. I WILL STRENGTHEN THEE, YEA I WILL HELP THEE.
Drawing; 4×92; signed A.E.R.G. delt. & sclpt.
Tracings; 38×38 and $17\frac{1}{2} \times 33$; October 1903.

18 Brass plate for Langport School, Somerset, recording the gift of bench and tools, by J. T. Knight, C.C., in the name of his two sons ASHTON & ARCHIBALD KNIGHT, O.L.'s., September 1903.
Size of plate: $7\frac{7}{8} \times 19\frac{3}{4}$; drawing signed A. E. R. Gill, 16 Old Buildings, Lincoln's Inn, W.C. (October, 1903).

19 Inscription in St. David's Church, Exeter. Oct. 1903.
[E.G. recorded this as having been done, but it has not been possible to obtain more detailed information concerning it.]

20 Tombstone in Nunhead Cemetery, Kent, in memory of ANNIE GILL, 1858–1879, and of her father The Revd. GEORGE GILL, 1820–1880, for 16 years Missionary in the South Sea Islands and 19 years Minister of the Westgate Congregational Chapel, Burnley. Also of SARAH, his wife, 1818–1898.

Rubbing of stone; $58\frac{1}{4} \times 29\frac{1}{2}$; November 1903.

[George and Sarah Gill were Eric Gill's grandparents.]   [*See Plate III*]

20A Alphabet designed for cutting in stone.

Outline drawing of $2\frac{1}{2}$ in. letters; signed A. E. R. Gill, 1903 November.

A note reads: 'Dedicated to E.F.M. Being the best I can do at this time, therefore dedicated as above.'

[*N.B.* 'E.F.M.' refers to Ethel Foster Moore his future wife.]

21 Lettering for inscription on metal: HE THAT BELIEVETH IN CHRIST SHALL HAVE ETERNAL LIFE.

Pen and ink drawing of inscription; $10\frac{1}{2} \times 12\frac{1}{2}$; [n.d.] *c.* 1903.

22 Inscription incised on Hopton-Wood stone: GLORIA IN ALTISSIMIS DEO . . .

Rubbing; 17×29; 1903.

A description together with a collotype reproduction (Plate XXIV) will be found in Edward Johnston's *Writing and Illuminating and Lettering*, pp. 486–7. This tablet was for many years in the possession of E.G.'s father the Rev. A. T. Gill.

23 Inscription in Latin in memory of ARTHUR HAROLD WEBSTER, d. 1902.

Drawing; $40 \times 21\frac{3}{4}$; *c.* 1903.

[This drawing bears the following pencilled note: 'This was done under compulsion. A.E.R.G.']

24 Inscription in memory of MARY CONSTANCE SMITH, Deaconess, d. 1902.

Drawing; $15\frac{1}{2} \times 9$; *c.* 1903.

25 Lettering: ANNO CORONATIONIS ED. VII REG.

[Drawing marked 'Knightsbridge'.]

Tracing of portion of inscription; $24\frac{1}{2} \times 38$; signed, but undated, A. E. R. Gill, 16 Old Buildings, Lincoln's Inn, W.C.; *c.* 1903.

26 Gravestone, with relief inscription, in memory of WILLIAM HOUNSELL of Wykes Court, b. 20 Feb. 1820, d. 12 June 1903.
Full-size lay-out of lettering; 15×21.
Rubbing; $17\frac{3}{4} \times 23\frac{1}{2}$.
Work executed c. 1903.

27 Foundation stone, St. Bartholomew, Stamford Hill, London, N., Ascension Day, May, 1903.
Actual size: 18×36; drawing of portion of inscription; signed A. E. R. Gill, 16 Old Buildings, Lincoln's Inn, W.C.; undated, c. 1903.

28 Inscription for memorial to CICILIA ROBINSON, Deaconess, d. 9 September 1903, aged 33.
Drawing; $16\frac{1}{2} \times 9$; signed A. E. R. Gill, 16 Old Buildings, Lincoln's Inn, W.C.; c. 1903.

29 Tablet: THE HOME LIBRARY for W. H. Smith & Son, London.
Drawing of tablet; 3×21; signed: 'for W. H. Smith & Son, per Mr. Hornby. Jan. 22, 1903. A.E.R.G.'

30 Panel of 4 in. letters, cut in oak: STUDY QUIET.
Rubbing; 5×43; signed A. E. R. Gill, for Edward Johnston; 1904.

31 Painted letters on name board for the INNS OF COURT RIFLE VOLUNTEERS. March 1904.

32 Plaque recording the gift by the Mayor (Sir George Collard, Kt.) and Corporation of Canterbury of site for the War Memorial to 'THE BUFFS' and ROYAL EAST KENT IMPERIAL YEOMANRY in Danejohn Park, Canterbury.
Full-size drawing; $11\frac{1}{2} \times 64\frac{3}{4}$; signed A.E.R.G. 1904.
(See also No. 15.)

33 Foundation stone for the Whitefield Memorial Chapel, Tottenham Court Road, London, W. April, 1904.
[This chapel was totally destroyed in the bombing of London, 1940.]

34 Lettering for W. H. Smith and Son: FOR ADVERTISING SPACES ON THIS RAILWAY APPLY TO W. H. SMITH & SON 186 STRAND, LONDON, W.C. also: BOOKBINDING OF EVERY DESCRIPTION . . .
Work executed 1904.

35 Fascia for W. H. Smith & Son's bookshop at Clacton-on-Sea, Essex. June 1904.

36 Memorial tablet to HENRY W. RENDEL, b. Nov. 1866, d. May 1903. Drawing; $9\frac{1}{2} \times 13$; signed: 'A. E. R. Gill, 23 Old Buildings, Lincoln's Inn, W.C.' June 1904.

37 Foundation stone for the Working Men's College, Camden Town, London. LAID BY H.R.H. THE PRINCE OF WALES July 1904. In memory of FREDERICK DENISON MAURICE.
Rubbing; $23\frac{1}{2} \times 38\frac{1}{2}$; June 1904.

38 Memorial dedicated to the memory of WILLIAM PATON of the Royal Artillery, to commemorate his gallantry in action with the C Battery, E Brigade, R.H.A., at the battle of Maiwand, 1880, d. 15th May, 1904. Also in memory of his wife AGNES, who died June, 1904.
Rubbing; $38 \times 27\frac{1}{2}$; July 1904.

39 Fascia for W. H. Smith & Son's bookshop at Bournemouth. August 1904.

40 Tombstone at Ilkley, Yorks., in memory of ELIZABETH CATHERINE FLETCHER, d. 10 January 1904.
Drawing of inscription; $23 \times 13\frac{1}{4}$; September 1904.

41 Lettering: CLERGY TRAINING SCHOOL, in 4 in. caps., & WESTCOTT HOUSE in two lines of 6 in. caps., accompanied by a mitre, all letters carved in relief. This is in Cambridge.
Sketch; $\frac{1}{4}$ f-s.; signed Gill & Hewitt.
Rubbings of inscription; $12\frac{1}{4} \times 45\frac{1}{2}$ and $4 \times 52\frac{1}{4}$.
Work executed September 1904.

42 Tombstone with bronze plate in memory of EMMA SOPHIA GALTON.
Drawing of plate; $19 \times 6\frac{3}{4}$; September 1904.

43 Inscription in memory of Dean FREDERICK WILLIAM FARRAR, 1831–1903. September 1904.

44 Gravestone in cloister garth of Canterbury Cathedral in memory of Archbishop FREDERICK TEMPLE—1821–1902. October 1904.

45 Headstone in memory of PERCY ROBERT BASIL FEILDING, second son of the Seventh Earl of Denbigh, 1827–1904.
Rubbing of inscription; $24 \times 21\frac{1}{2}$; October 1904.

46 The Ten Commandments, in Holy Trinity Church, Charwelton, Rugby, painted in black on four panels above the high altar. Above the panels is an inscription, lettered in gilt: GOD SPAKE THESE WORDS AND SAID.
Work executed November 1904.

47 Foundation stone laid by Mrs. W. H. BROWN, 12 May 1904. The inscription reads: THIS STONE WAS / LAID ON MAY XII / MCMIV / BY MRS. H. BROWN / He shall make thee a joy / of many generations . . .
Rubbing; $25\frac{1}{2} \times 25\frac{1}{2}$; c. 1904.
[It has not been possible to trace the whereabouts of this work.]

48 Oak panel for the Hospital for Sick Children, Great Ormond Street, London, in memory of Nurse ELEANOR FIELD, for fifteen years at the Hospital and for thirteen years at the Nurses' Hostel. Died August 14 1903.
Drawing of inscription; $17 \times 24\frac{1}{2}$; [n.d.] c. 1904.

49 Memorial stone laid by JOHN HENNELL, B.A., 9 July, 1904.
Rubbing; $18 \times 33\frac{1}{2}$; c. 1904.
This stone is 'signed' 'A.E.R.G.'.

50 Tablet of incised letters: G.E.O., LL.D. VICARIUS MCMIV.
Rubbing; $9 \times 12\frac{1}{2}$; c. 1904.

51 Tablet at Laurence Sheriff School, Rugby, in memory of HENRY VICTOR WHITEHOUSE, 1889–1904.
Work executed c. 1904.

52 Foundation stone for the Mission Hall of the GOOD SHEPHERD and TEMPLE INSTITUTE in Garrett's Lane, Wandsworth, laid by Beatrice Blanche Temple, October 1905.
Rubbing; $16\frac{3}{4} \times 25\frac{3}{4}$; 1905.

53 Carving in St. John the Divine, Richmond, Surrey. February 1905.

54 Numerals for Hymn Boards for St. John the Divine, Richmond, Surrey.
Full-size drawing; $8\frac{1}{2} \times 15$; February 1905.

55 Fascia for W. H. Smith & Son's bookshop at Leicester. March 1905.

56 Fascia for W. H. Smith & Son's bookshop at Southport. March 1905.

57 Inscription in Latin on stone tablet in Ante-chapel of Brasenose College, Oxford, in memory of ALBERTI WATSON, d. November 1904.
Pencil drawing; signed A. E. R. Gill, 1, Upper Cheyne Walk, Chelsea, S.W. 22 Mar. 1905.
Rubbing; 20¾ × 35; signed A. E. R. Gill.

58 Incised tablet in memory of HENRY CROMPTON. 1836–1904.
Full-size drawing; 6½ × 14¾; April 1905.

59 Painted notice board for the Parish Church of St. John, Bognor Regis. April 1905.

60 Inscription on fountain at Newnham College, Cambridge, in memory of HENRY SIDGWICK, 1905.
Drawing; 22½ in. diameter; c. April 1905.

61 Painted letters on fascia and signboards for W. H. Smith & Son's shop at Moseley, Birmingham.
Pencil drawings; scale 1 in. to 1 ft.; signed A. E. R. Gill, 1 Upper Cheyne Row, S.W. May 1905.

62 Fascia for W. H. Smith & Son's bookshop at Scarborough. May 1905.

63 Inscription for the University College of South Wales and Monmouth, Cardiff. May 1905.

64 Tombstone in Cambridge in memory of . . . CLOUGH. May 1905.

65 Inscription recording the gift of the plans of a church (in Melbourne, Australia?) in memory of CAROLINE LOUISA LYON.
Rubbing; 15¾ × 15½; May 1905.

66 Brass tablet in St. Wilfred's Church, Bognor Regis, in memory of JAMES ALLEN FREEBORN HOWELL, 1887–1904.
Rubbing; 17 × 15½; May 1905.
[This tablet was the joint work of Eric Gill, and his brother Macdonald.]

67 Stone tablet in porch of St. Bartholomew, Brightwell Baldwin, Oxon., in memory of RICHARD DU CANE, d. January 1904.
Rubbing; 9 × 15; July 1905.
(See also No. 88.)

68 Tombstone at Clovelly, Devonshire, in memory of MARY CHRISTINE MANNERS, daughter of John, Lord Manners & of Constance his wife. Died at Bangalore, India, 15 February 1904. Aged 17 years.
Rubbing of inscription: $18\frac{3}{4} \times 26\frac{1}{2}$; August 1905.
(See also No. 97.)

69 Tombstone, at Kingussie, Inverness-shire, in memory of LUCY McEWEN, 1857–1904.
Rubbing; $13\frac{1}{2} \times 27\frac{1}{4}$; September 1905.

70 Tablet beneath stone seat from Rochester Cathedral built by Bishop Gundulf, d. 1108. The inscription reads: THE CATHEDRAL CHURCH/ OF CHRIST & OUR LADY OF/ ROCHESTER SENDS GREETING / WITH THE ABOVE STONE FROM / BP. GUNDULF'S CATHE-DRAL:/ A.D. 1074.
[This, it is believed, is in a Cathedral in Australia.]
Rubbing; $8\frac{3}{4} \times 11\frac{1}{2}$; September 1905.

71 Signboard at Stoke-on-Trent for JOSIAH WEDGWOOD Ltd. October 1905.

72 Brass nameplates for 29B Lincoln's Inn Fields, London, W.C., lettered ALFRED H. POWELL.
Rubbings; $4\frac{3}{4} \times 11\frac{3}{4}$, $1\frac{1}{4} \times 6$ and $4\frac{1}{2} \times 10\frac{1}{4}$; December 1905.
[E.G. also designed a nameplate for Alfred H. Powell (architect), for his house in Red Lion Square, 1906.]

73 Relief inscription on Hopton-Wood stone: PAX HUIC DOMUI.
Rubbing; $9 \times 8\frac{1}{2}$; c. 1905.

74 Relief inscription on Hopton-Wood stone: SUSSEX HOUSE for Emery Walker's workshop in Hampshire Hog Lane, Hammersmith, London, W.
Rubbing; 10×15; 1905.

75 Brass plate for window in memory of EDWARD PREST of York, his wife and eldest daughter, also of JAMES WILLIAMSON, d. July 1899, and of C. G. WALE, second daughter of E. PREST, d. January 1905.
Rubbing; $8\frac{1}{2} \times 17\frac{1}{4}$; c. 1905.

76 Letters 'I O' incised on stone. Letters 2 in. high beneath which is a cross. Also inscribed: 'I. A.E.R.G. 9. 05.'
Rubbing; $5\frac{1}{2} \times 3\frac{3}{4}$; September 1905.

77 Tablet of Hopton-Wood stone with incised inscription: IN PRINCIPIO/ ERAT VERBUM ET / VERBUM ERAT APUD / DEUM ET DEUS ERAT VERBUM.
Rubbing of tablet; 8×13; dated by E.G.'s hand 1905.
This was cut for exhibition purposes.

77A Hopton-Wood stone tablet inscribed: DASS WIR UNS IN IHR ZERSTREUEN DARUM IST DIE WELT SO GROSS.
This was cut, presumably as an Exhibition piece, c. 1905.

78 Inscription on Hopton-Wood stone: ☧ Ω NON EST
Rubbing of inscription; $9\frac{3}{4} \times 15$; unsigned but dated by E.G. 1905.
[The compiler is in some doubt as to the meaning or purport of this inscription. It has been suggested to him that it is probably some cabalistic or alchemical rebus.]

79 Headstone with relief inscription on grit stone in memory of LILY FRANCES KATHERINE, wife of John Colquhoun Duff, d. 30 August 1905.
Rubbing; $23\frac{1}{2} \times 20$; c. 1906.

80 Tablet commemorating the gift of cross and candlesticks in memory of HENRY CHARLES RICHARDS, K.C., M.P., d. 1905.
Rubbing; $5\frac{1}{2} \times 28\frac{3}{4}$; c. 1906.

81 Inscription in memory of FREDERICK GEORGE HUME SMITH, Rector, St. Batholomew, Armley, Leeds, d. 1905.
Rubbing; $10\frac{3}{4} \times 11\frac{3}{4}$; c. 1906.

82 Gravestone of Portland stone, surmounted by a Celtic cross with relief inscription in memory of CAROLINE FRANCIS—1824–1905.
Rubbing; $36\frac{1}{4} \times 23\frac{3}{4}$; c. 1906.

83 Inscriptions for gateway of the W. H. SMITH MEMORIAL HALL and a sunk panel: ERECTED AS A WORKMEN'S CLUB IN MEMORY OF W. H. SMITH, M.P.
Sketch; $14\frac{3}{4} \times 22\frac{1}{4}$; signed A. E. R. Gill.

Another inscription: THIS HALL IS ERECTED IN MEMORY OF THE RIGHT HONOURABLE W. H. SMITH, M.P.
Rubbing; $17\frac{1}{2} \times 49$; c. 1906.
[Exhaustive enquiries have failed to produce any information as to the whereabouts of this Hall.]

84 Incised inscription on stone: ST. DYFRIG'S CLERGY HOUSE. In Fitzsimmon's Place, Cardiff.
Rubbing; $4\frac{3}{4} \times 29\frac{3}{4}$; January 1906.
(See also No. 118.)

85 Cruciform tombstone at Torquay in memory of THOMAS RIDGWAY BRIDSON, 1823–1904.
Rubbing of inscription; 30×9; April 1906.

86 Tombstone in St. Marylebone Cemetery, London, N.W., in memory of HENRY PRINCE, 1831–1906.
Rubbing of inscription; $6\frac{1}{2} \times 15\frac{3}{4}$; May 1906.

87 Circular stone tablet in Brompton Cemetery, London, S.W., in memory of EDWARD HUGHES, d. 1876, and of his son WILLIAM ARTHUR HUGHES, d. 1899.
Rubbing of inscription; circle 15 in. diameter; May 1906.

87A Tablet at Upton-on-Severn, Worcs., in memory of GEORGE EDWARD MARTIN, of Ham Court, 1829–1905. Commemorating the dedication of a window given by his friends.
Rubbing; $54 \times 23\frac{3}{4}$; c. 1906.
(See also No. 287.)

88 Cross in memory of RICHARD DU CANE, d. January 1904, and of his wife CHARLOTTE MARIA, d. June 1902.
Pencil drawing and rubbing; both $12\frac{1}{2} \times 14$; undated and unsigned.
Work executed May 1906.
(See also No. 67.)
[The whereabouts of this memorial is not known.]

89 Inscriptions in the Chapel of the Ascension, Hyde Park Place, London, W. This work, carried out in June 1906, was commissioned by Frederic Shields (d. 1911) whose elaborate Scriptural decorations adorn this building.
[The chapel was severely damaged in an air raid during the Second World War.]

90 Brass plate, THE NEW ENGLISH ART CLUB, New Bond Street, London.
Full-size drawing of lettering; $13\frac{3}{4} \times 12$; June 1906.
[This work was commissioned by William Rothenstein.]

91 Nameplate, 'A. RANDALL WELLS, Architect'.
Rubbing; $3\frac{1}{2} \times 9\frac{3}{4}$; June 1906.

92 Foundation stone (14×26) on left side of the entrance to the Y.M.C.A., Bold Street, Ealing, London, W.5, laid by the Duke of Argyle 7 July, 1906.
Inscription cut 29 June 1906.
(See also No. 116.)

93 Marble inscription, St. Laurence, Upminster, in memory of BRYDGES ROBINSON BRANFILL, J.P., 1833–1905.
Rubbing (mounted on card); $11\frac{3}{4} \times 12$; 1906.

94 Tombstone, with cross, at Leamington in memory of JAMES CHARLES WHITEHORNE, 1896–1905.
Pen and ink drawing of front and side elevations; signed A. E. R. Gill. 22 June 1906. Another pencil drawing (tinted); signed A. E. R. Gill. Aug. 1906.
Rubbing; $11\frac{1}{4} \times 15$.

95 Inscriptions of gilded letters in St. Luke's Church, Old Street, London. 1906.
The Church has since been demolished.

96 Monument in St. Helen's Church, Escrick, Yorks., showing Coat of Arms and inscription in memory of STEPHEN WILLOUGHBY LAWLEY, 1823–1905, third son of Paul Beilby, Lord Wenlock, Rector of Escrick, 1848–1868, and sometime Sub-dean of York. The inscription also records the building of this church and Rectory House.
Rubbing of tablet; $40\frac{1}{2} \times 50\frac{1}{2}$; two f-s. drawings (arms in colour), one of which is signed A. E. R. Gill, Hammersmith Terrace, W., Aug. 1906.
The name 'Wenlock' in the bottom right-hand corner ends with a flourished 'k' in which are embodied E.G.'s initials and the date 1907, thus, this is one of the few works actually 'signed' by him.

97 Inscription (letters in red), surmounted by a Coat of Arms in colour, in All Saints, Thorney Hill, Christchurch, Hants., commissioned by John, Lord

Manners and his wife, in memory of their daughter MARY CHRISTINE MANNERS who died at Bangalore in her eighteenth year, February 1904.
Actual size of the inscription (which is incised on the wall); 73 × 41.
Rubbing; dated August 1906.
(See also No. 68.)   [*See Plate IV*]

98 Zinc memorial tablet, in St. John the Baptist Hospital, Winchester, in memory of HENRY JOHN WICKHAM (1889–1898) and FREDERICK PEERS WICKHAM (1899–1904) Chaplains of this hospital.
Drawing; 7 × 14½; September 1906.

99 Gravestone at St. Mary Magdalene's, North Ockendon, Upminster, Essex, in memory of CHAMPION RUSSELL, 1820–1887.
Pencil drawing; 10½ × 11¾; July 1906.
Rubbing of inscription; 11¾ × 13.

100 Cruciform tombstone at Farncombe, nr. Godalming in memory of THEODOSIUS STUART RUSSELL. Captain Chief Constable of the West Riding of Yorkshire, 1876–1905. Born 1836, died 1906.
Pencil drawing (tinted); signed A. E. R. Gill, 8 Aug. 1906.
Rubbing of inscription; 24¾ × 34½.
Additional inscription: In memory of LOUISA CHARLOTTE EMILY his wife, 1847–1923.
Rubbing; 32 × 17½; 1924.

101 Sign for W. H. Smith & Son at 95 Fetter Lane, London, E.C. September 1906.
[Building since demolished.]

102 Inscription on pedestal of statue in Portland Place, London, W., erected by members of the Regent Street Polytechnic in memory of QUINTIN HOGG, 1845–1903. Sculptor: George Frampton.
Drawing (for inscription); 14 × 10; signed A. E. R. Gill, Calligrapher. 1906.
Work executed November 1906.

103 Inscription on Hopton-Wood stone in memory of ELIZA, 1814–1906, widow of the Rev. Chambre Corker Townshend of Derry, Rosscarbery, Co. Cork.
Rubbing of inscription; 25½ × 25; June 1907.

104 Hopton-Wood stone tablet on wall of shooting box on the Hempstead Estate, Holt, Norfolk, in memory of SAMUEL FOWLE, 1830–1906. Keeper on the estate for forty-five years.
Rubbing; 24 × 22; work executed December 1906.
This work was commissioned by Edward Johnston who designed the inscription.

105 Inscription in memory of Rev. HENRY GEORGE WATKINS, of Parkstone, Dorset, d. March 1906.
Rubbing; 32¼ × 16½; [n.d.] c. 1906.

106 Gravestone in memory of ALICE ELIZABETH BUSK. 1848–1906.
F-s. drawing of portion of inscription; 13 × 90¾; [n.d.] c. 1906.

107 Inscription in memory of HELOISE DE MAILLY REIGHLEY, d. July 1906.
Rubbing; 17 × 10¾; [n.d.] c. 1906.

108 Inscription in memory of FLORENCE EMMA STEVENS d. July 1906.
Rubbing; 11¼ × 29½; [n.d.] c. 1906.

109 Inscription in memory of H. E. TUFNELL, d. September 1906.
Rubbing; 3 × 7½; [n.d.] c. 1906.

110 Stone tablet, inscription surmounted by Coat of Arms, in North Transept, St. John, Stone, nr. Aylesbury, in memory of General Sir HENRY AUGUSTUS SMYTH, K.C.M.G., 1826–1906, Colonel Commandant Royal Artillery & sometime Governor & Commander-in-Chief of Malta.
Pencil drawing; signed A. E. R. Gill. Hammersmith Terrace. 30 Jan. '07.
Size of tablet: 56⅜ × 27. Rubbing of complete memorial with another rubbing showing 'OCT' corrected to 'SEPT'—the former still visible in outline.
[The inscription on lower portion of tablet is by another hand.]
(See No. 127.)   [See Plate VII]

111 Wooden tablet on S. wall of nave in All Saints', Thelwall, Warrington, in memory of EDWARD THE ELDER (870–924) who, in the year 923, built the fortress and town of Thelwall. The tablet also commemorates the coronation of EDWARD VII in 1902.
It consists of a central panel (22½ × 18¾) with background painted as a *trompe-l'œil* of vellum nailed at the corners, lettered mostly in black, capital letters in

red with flourishes in red and green. This is supported on a panel and surmounted by a panel carrying a coronet. Overall height: 57 in. There are two
side panels (28 × 10¾ each) the lettering raised in gesso and gilt; blue ground.
That on the left is 'signed' at foot: 'Fecit Helfer Bros., London W'; that on
the right is 'signed': 'F. C. Eden, Architect'.
Rubbings of panel inscriptions; (left) 21 × 11, (right) 24½ × 11; undated and
unsigned.
Work executed January–March 1907.

112 Oval tablet of white marble set in an alabaster frame, St. Mary, Bridport,
in memory of HARRIET TEMPLER, 1817–1905.
F-s. drawing; 42 × 35; signed 1907 A.E.R.G.

113 EVER THE DISCOURAGED RESOLUTE STRUGGLING
SOUL OF MAN EVER THE SOUL DISSATISFIED CURIOUS
UNCONVINCED AT LAST STRUGGLING TO-DAY THE SAME
BATTLING THE SAME . . .
On base of statue by Frederick Lessore for the Royal Academy exhibition.
Cut by E.G. March 1907.

114 Memorial tablet in Nunhead Cemetery, Kent, in memory of ANNIE
PHELPS.
[Mrs. Phelps was the charwoman for Eric and Macdonald Gill at 16 Old
Buildings, Lincoln's Inn. The tablet, executed in March 1907, was destroyed
in the bombing of 1940.]

115 Memorial plate for RICHARD COE. March 1907.
[E.G. recorded doing this but it has not been possible to obtain more detailed
information concerning it.]

116 Stone (14 × 26) commemorating the opening of the Y.M.C.A., Bold
Street, Ealing, London, W.5, by Lord Kinnaird, 17 April 1907. This is on the
right side of entrance.
Inscription cut 8 April 1907.
(See also No. 92.)

117 Signboard for Katharine Adams [bookbinder].
This work, commissioned by Emery Walker, was for Miss Adams's bindery at
Weston-sub-Edge, Broadway, Worcs.
April 1907.

C

118 Foundation Stone commemorating the completion of St. Dyfrig's Church, Wood Street, Cardiff. Laid by Mrs. Jenner on St. Mark's Day, 1907.
Rubbing; $21\frac{1}{2} \times 22$; April 1907.
(See also No. 84.)

119 Headstone (Portland) in memory of JOHN KIPLING—1843–1906. Head gardener at Knebworth House, Herts.
Rubbing; $36\frac{1}{4} \times 22$; April 1907.
[This work was commissioned by the Earl of Lytton.]

119A Stone tablet, letters incised: PUBLIC HOUSE TRUST. This was commissioned by the Earl of Lytton.
Work executed April 1907.

120 Foundation stone for Rectory at Finningham, Stowmarket, Suffolk, in memory of TEMPLE FRERE, Rector of Finningham, 1805–1829, laid by Winifred, daughter of John Tudor Frere.
F-s. detail; $24 \times 22\frac{1}{2}$; signed A. E. R. Gill, 16 April, 1907.

121 Inscription on Hopton-Wood stone on sarcophagus in King Chapel, Ockham, Woking, of RALPH GORDON NOEL MILBANKE, D.L., 2nd EARL of LOVELACE—1839–1906.
Rubbing; $11\frac{3}{4} \times 24\frac{3}{4}$; May 1907.
(See also No. 169.)

122 Memorial to Major JOHN SEYMOUR WYNNE FINCH, d. January 1906.
Drawings; signed A. E. R. Gill, June 1907.
Rubbing; $16\frac{1}{2} \times 31\frac{3}{4}$.

123 Tablet in St. Andrew's Roker, Sunderland, commemorating the building of the main fabric of the church, in 1906–1907, in memory of JANE PRIESTMAN. Dedicated 19 July 1907.
Rubbing; $11\frac{1}{2} \times 24\frac{1}{2}$; June 1907.

124 Bronze tablet for the Borough Polytechnic, Southwark, London. June 1907.

125 Relief inscription on monument at Ryde, Isle of Wight, in memory of IRENE NICHOLS, 1862–1907, elder daughter of Francis Morgan & Mary Nichols.
Rubbing of inscription; $13\frac{1}{4} \times 54$; June 1907.

126 Tablet on house (in Leamington) built for A. & M. Whitehorne.
Rubbing; $6\frac{3}{4} \times 24\frac{1}{4}$; July 1907.

127 Tablet at Woolwich in memory of General Sir HENRY AUGUSTUS
SMYTH K.C.M.G., d. September 1906.
Pencil drawing $\frac{1}{8}$th f-s., undated, but signed A. E. R. Gill.
Rubbing; $41\frac{3}{4} \times 18\frac{1}{2}$.
Work executed 1907.
(See also No. 110.)

128 Tablet of incised letters, at Painswick, Stroud, Glos.: THE PAINS-
WICK INSTITUTE FOUNDED BY MRS. MARY FRANCES
SARAH WILLIAMS, 1906.
Rubbing; $6\frac{3}{4} \times 26$; September 1907.
[The tablet is on the inside of the porch of the Institute.]

129 Six foundation stones for St. John's Hospital, Morden Hill, Lewisham,
S.E.13, of which the following is typical: 'This Porch was given In Memoriam
R.M.C. 1907.'
Size of stones: 36×36; September–October 1907.

130 Bronze tablet in St. Martin's Church, Kensal Rise, London, in memory
of the Reverend A. McLEAN HANLEY. October 1907.

131 Inscription on wood for reredos in St. John the Divine, Richmond,
Surrey. November 1907.

132 Memorial of Hopton-Wood stone, 12 ft. × 9 ft., on the wall near the
Oxford staircase, Ladies' College, Cheltenham, in memory of DOROTHEA
BEALE, LL.D., 1831–1906, Principal of the college, 1858–1906.
The joint work of Eric and Macdonald Gill, c. 1907.
(See also No. 133.)

133 Tablet on South side of Lady Chapel of Gloucester Cathedral, in memory
of DOROTHEA BEALE, LL.D., 1831–1906, Principal of The Ladies'
College, Cheltenham 1858–1906.
Rubbing of inscription; $16\frac{1}{2} \times 88\frac{3}{4}$; c. 1907.
(See also No. 132.)

134 Oval memorial tablet in St. Bartholomew's Hospital, London in memory
of JACOBI ANDREW. fl. 1897.
Pen and ink drawing; $4\frac{1}{4} \times 5\frac{1}{4}$; c. 1907.

135 Monument erected by the 2nd Battalion The Buffs in memory of Colonel EDGAR EVELYN RAVENHILL, D.S.O., who died at Wynberg, Cape Colony, February 6, 1907, aged 47.
Rubbing; 21 × 19; [n.d.] c. 1907.

136 Inscription for stone laid by Gertrude and Lawrence Squire, 1 November 1907.
Rubbing; 6¼ × 26; [n.d.] c. 1907.

137 Gravestone of red Mansfield stone, surmounted by a cross, the inscription in relief, in memory of THOMAS DOLLING BOLTON—1843–1906.
Rubbing; 20¾ × 25; [n.d.] c. 1907.
[Work executed in collaboration with his brother Macdonald Gill.]

138 Hopton-Wood stone tablet, inscription in relief, in memory of GERTRUDE EMILY CUNNINGHAM-FOOT, 1872–1899.
Drawing; 15 × 14; [n.d.] c. 1907.

139 Foundation stone in the Children's Ward of the Essex County Hospital, Colchester: THIS WAS LAID WITH MASONIC CEREMONIAL BY COLONEL THE RIGHT HONOURABLE MARK LOCKWOOD, P.C., C.V.O., M.P., GRAND MASTER OF THE FREEMASONS OF ESSEX.
Rubbing; unsigned and undated; 15¾ × 35½.
Work executed 1907.

140 Brass tablet in entrance hall of the CENTRAL FOUNDATION GIRLS SCHOOL, Spital Square, Bishopsgate, London E.1, recording the history of the school.
Rubbing; 19 × 45½; [n.d.] c. 1907.

141 Tablet in memory of WILLIAM MAUNSELL REEVES of Ebbisham House, Epsom, d. 21 February 1907.
Rubbing; 8¾ × 20½; [n.d.] c. 1907.

142 Bronze tablet in Cape Town Cathedral in memory of FYDELL EDMUND GARRETT, 1865–1907.
Sketch; 24 × 25½; January 1908.

143 Gilding and carving reredos, St. Batholomew and St. Christopher, Haslemere. January 1908.

144 Stone tablet S. DUBRITIUS, LLANVACHES, nr. Newport, Mon., commemorating the restoration of the church by Godfrey Charles Morgan, 1st Viscount Tredegar.
Rubbing; $11\frac{3}{4} \times 18\frac{3}{4}$; [n.d.] c. 1908.

145 Inscription: AN GRAF KESSLER MCMVIII on the upper of two boards ($9\frac{1}{2} \times 6\frac{1}{2}$) intended for a case to contain a Memorial Address written on vellum by Edward Johnston. The work is 'signed', on the underside of the upper board 'A. E. R. Gill carver'.
Rubbing; $7\frac{1}{4} \times 6\frac{1}{4}$; March 1908.
[Now in the collection of Evan R. Gill.]

146 Brass tablet in entrance hall of The Central Foundation Girls' School, Spital Square, Bishopsgate, London, E.1, in memory of the Reverend WILLIAM ROGERS, d. 1896.
Rubbing; $8\frac{3}{4} \times 26\frac{1}{4}$.
Work executed April 1908.

147 Notice Board for KING'S COLLEGE HOSPITAL, Denmark Hill, London, S.E. April 1908.
(See also Nos. 182, 190 and 269.)

148 Panels on either side of fireplace in the Board Room, York City & County Bank. Lettered (left) Y.C. & C.B. and (right) A.D. 1908.
Size of each panel: $7 \times 8\frac{1}{4}$.
Tracing of full-size details of letters; signed L.Mc.D.G[ill], 25.5.08.
[In this work Macdonald Gill collaborated with his brother.]

149 Tablet in memory of Colonel PERCY RALPH RICARDO, C.B., Commandant of the Victoria Military Forces, died June 4, 1907 aged 51, and was buried at Melbourne, Australia. He served in S. Africa during the Boer War in command of the Queensland Mounted Infantry a regiment he raised some years previously.
Drawing of inscription; $28 \times 17\frac{1}{2}$; signed A. E. R. Gill. Hammersmith Terrace, W. February 1908.
Work executed May 1908.

150 Inscription on font in St. Mary's Parish Church, Hornsey, London, the gift of Evan Hare, November 1899.
Rubbing; $10\frac{3}{4} \times 16\frac{1}{4}$; signed A. E. R. Gill, 16 Old Buildings, Lincoln's Inn, W.C. May 1908.

151 Memorial panel on granite boulder over grave in Logie Coldstone Churchyard, near Dinnet, Aberdeenshire, in memory of GEORGE CHRISTOPHER CARTER, d. November 1907.
Full-size detail drawing; $8\frac{7}{8} \times 10\frac{3}{4}$; signed A. E. R. Gill.
Another f-s. detail drawing (tinted) with notes; unsigned and undated.
Work executed May 1908.

152 Nameboard 'WAYSIDE' in Cavendish Avenue. A painted inscription for the first house occupied by Sir Sydney Cockerell, in Cambridge. June 1908.

153 Tablet, the inscription in relief, in memory of FRANCES POWER COBBE, 1822–1904.
Rubbing; $4\frac{1}{2} \times 15\frac{3}{4}$.
Work executed June 1908.

154 Marble tablet in St. Egwin's Church, Norton, near Evesham, in memory of MARY BEATRICE BOULTER, daughter of Walter Consitt Boulter, who died 12 March 1902, in her 21st year.
Rubbing; $30\frac{1}{4} \times 19\frac{3}{4}$; July 1908.   [See Plate VIII]

155 Headstone in the graveyard of St. Mary's Church, South Road, St. Mary's, Adelaide, S. Australia, in memory of WILLIAM SAMUEL MOORE, d. 1900, Rector of this parish 1884–1900.
Rubbing; $15\frac{3}{4} \times 15\frac{3}{4}$; July 1908.

156 Tablet in St. Dubritius', Llanvaches, Newport, Mon., for screen erected September 1908, in memory of ROSAMOND EMILY LINDSAY, d. March 1908.
Rubbing; $10\frac{1}{4} \times 15$; July 1908.

157 Tombstone at St. Paul's, Over Tabley, Knutsford, Cheshire, in memory of HENRY LEWIS BROOKE LANGFORD-BROOKE, 1840–1907.
Drawing for floreated carving above the inscription (designed by L. Macdonald Gill); $32\frac{1}{4} \times 23\frac{1}{2}$; August, 1908.
Rubbing of inscription; $12\frac{3}{4} \times 17\frac{1}{2}$; March 1909.

158 Portland headstone in memory of JOHANNES PITT, 1806–1908, Chief Constable of the County of Sussex, 1880–1885. Also in memory of his wife ELIZABETH.

Pencil drawing (coloured); signed A. E. R. Gill, 16 Old Buildings, Lincoln's Inn, W.C. Sept. 1908.
Approximate size of stone: 72 × 78.

159 Stone plaque commemorating the Golden Wedding of Andrew and Charlotte Johnston of Woodford Green, Essex.
Rubbing; 16 × 21; September 1908.
[Andrew Johnston, M.P., J.P., was the uncle of Edward Johnston.]

160 Headstone of three panels in Hopton-Wood stone in Hanwell Cemetery, in memory of NANCY ANNIE EMILY HEAL, 1881–1907.
Rubbing; $27\frac{1}{4}$ × 18; September 1908.

161 Foundation stone for CONGREGATIONAL CHURCH, CHARL-TON, KENT, laid by Rev. S. Lloyd-Davies, Pastor, 29 October, 1908.
Half full-size setting-out; undated but signed A. E. R. Gill.
Rubbing; $11\frac{3}{4}$ × $17\frac{3}{4}$; 1908.

162 Tombstone in memory of JOHN BERRY of Westerbogie & Inverdovat-Tayfield, 1725–1817. And of JANET FRASER his wife, 1731–1762. And of ISABELLA LAW of Pitillock his second wife, 1739–1807. And of MARGARET BERRY, 1781–1864. And of SARAH CRAWFURD BERRY, 1782–1880.
Drawing; 11 × 6; signed A.E.R.G. Oct. 30 '08.

163 Foundation stone laid by the Rev. R. Fotheringham, Chairman, London Congregational Union, 1908.
Pencil drawing; $6\frac{1}{4}$ × 17; signed A. E. R. Gill, 16 Old Buildings, Lincoln's Inn, W.C. (Nov. 6, '08)
Rubbing of top part of inscription; $4\frac{3}{4}$ × 17.

164 Painted letters: HEARTH.
Full-size detail; 10 × 30; signed A. E. R. Gill. 12 Nov. '08.
[This was commissioned by the Earl of Lytton for Knebworth House.]

165 Inscription, in Latin, beneath a picture in Eton College in memory of EDMOND WARRE, C.B., C.V.O., Provost of Eton, 1884–1905.
Rubbing of inscription; $7\frac{1}{4}$ × $7\frac{1}{2}$; Dec., 1908.

166 Brass tablet in memory of SAMUEL NATHANIEL ELLIOT, d. 12 August 1903.
Rubbing; 10 × 19¼; [n.d.] c. 1908.

167 Inscription above entrance to Lodging Home for Working Women, Portman House.
This was one of the Shaftesbury Institutes, also known as Miss Meredith Brown's Homes. Portman House was 21 and 23 Harrow Street, Lisson Grove, London, N.W.
Work executed c. 1908.
[Harrow Street has since been demolished.]

168 Monument in Kensal Green Cemetery, London, in memory of WILLIAM SMITH WILLIAMS, 1820–1906, and MARGARET ELIZA-BETH WILLIAMS, his widow.
Pencil drawing (tinted); 4½ × 9; signed A.E.R.G. 27.3.09.

168A Hopton-Wood stone panel with Roman capitals, incised with 'V' section.
This alphabet was carved for Edward Johnston in April 1909 from which collotype reproductions were made for his portfolio *Manuscript & Inscription Letters*, first published by John Hogg, London, September 1909. (Now published by Sir Isaac Pitman & Sons, Ltd.) This is Plate 13 of the portfolio.
Size of the original; 10½ × 15¾. A reproduction was also published (1936) by the Victoria & Albert Museum as No. 1 of a series of four Lettering Sheets. Plaster casts of this panel (11¼ × 16⅞) were sold by John Hogg, London.

168B Hopton-Wood stone panel with lower case italics and numerals, incised with 'V' section.
This is one of the three alphabets carved for Edward Johnston in April 1909. For details of subsequent reproductions see No. 168a. This is Plate 14 of the portfolio and No. 2 of the Lettering Sheets.

168C Hopton-Wood stone panel with raised capitals and numerals.
This was the third of the three alphabets carved for Edward Johnston in April 1909. See Nos. 168a and 168b. This was reproduced as Plate 15 of the portfolio of *Manuscript & Inscription Letters*.
Plaster casts of this panel (10⅜ × 15⅝) were sold by John Hogg, London, who published the portfolio, 1909.

169 Inscribed tablet in remembrance of Ralph, EARL OF LOVELACE, 1839–1906, for cottages the property of the Countess of Lovelace.
Rubbing; 4 × 189½; 1909.
(See also No. 121.)

170 Inscriptions for brass plates: SWINBURNE, O'GORMAN & BAILLIE of 82 Victoria Street, London, S.W. 1909.

171 Cruciform headstone for . . . ALWYN with foliage sculpture.
Outline of background; 26½ × 20¾; 7 May 1909.
[It has not been possible to obtain further information concerning this work.]

172 Foundation stone for Romford Institute. 1909.

173 Headstone in memory of WILLIAM SHERWOOD, d. March 1909.
Rubbing of inscription; 10 × 20¾; [n.d.] c. May 1909.

174 Panel inscribed with the names of the Clerks of the Peace, Northallerton, Yorks.
Rubbing; 16¼ × 37¼; 1909.

175 Inscription above a tap in Mells, Somerset: FOR THE USE OF MELLS VILLAGE IN MEMORY OF MARK HORNER 1908.
F-s. setting-out; 21¼ in diameter; signed A. E. R. Gill, 16 Old Buildings, Lincoln's Inn, W.C.2. 3 May 1909.
Another drawing (neither signed nor dated) of a projected inscription reads: MARK GEORGE HORNER WHO DIED ON MARCH THE THIRD NINETEEN HUNDRED AND EIGHT AGED SIXTEEN.
(Cf. No. 176.)

176 Waterhouse (or Memorial Well) designed by Sir Edwin Lutyens, at Mells, Somerset, bearing an inscription: FOR THE USE OF MELLS VILLAGE IN MEMORY OF MARK HORNER 1908.
The wording of this inscription is identical with that for the Memorial Tap.
(Cf. No. 175.)

177 Tombstone in white marble in memory of SOPHIE L. A. KESSLER, Geb. in Frankfurt-A-M., 23 Jan, 1854. Gest in London 24 Feb. 1909.
Pencil drawing; undated.
Rubbing; 8¾ × 11½; [n.d.] c. 1909.

178 Head and foot stones of Portland stone, at Broughty Ferry, Dundee, in memory of ROSE TICHENER, 1880–1908.
Six pencil drawings (coloured) the first five of which are lettered (A)–E; signed A.E.R.G. 27.3.09. The sixth, a scale drawing, is signed A. E. R. Gill, Ditchling Common. May 17 '09.

179 Chronogram inscription: SCVTIFERI GENERI LVX VITAE . . . for a lintel at 'Little Croft', Steventon, Abingdon, Berks, the residence of G. F. Squire.
Rubbing; $10\frac{1}{4} \times 21\frac{1}{4}$; May 1909.

180 Headstone in the City of London and Tower Hamlets Cemetery, Mile End Road, London, E., for grave No. T992.
Drawing; 10×12; signed L. McD. Gill delt. 20.v.09.

181 Tablet of white marble on a black stone base in St. Maelog, Llandyfaelog, Carmarthenshire, commemorating the ministry of the Rev. PETER WILLIAMS, Annotator and Publisher of the Welsh Bible. Born at West-marsh, Llansadurnen, 1723; died and buried at Llandyfaelog, 1796.
Full-size setting-out for proposed inscription; signed A.E.R.G. June 09.
Size of tablet: 36×51.

182 Foundation stone for King's College Hospital, Denmark Hill, London, S.E., laid by King Edward VII.
Full-size pencil drawing (tinted); signed A. E. R. Gill. July 1909.
Rubbing of inscription; $20\frac{1}{2} \times 23\frac{3}{4}$; signed Eric Gill 1909.
(See also Nos. 147, 190 and 269.)

183 Foundation Stones for Sutton Adult School, Sutton, Surrey, laid 21 July 1909 by Mrs. R. C. Henderson, Thomas Wall and R. C. Forster.
Rubbings; (respectively) $7 \times 30\frac{3}{4}$, $12\frac{1}{4} \times 28$ and 18×29; 1909.

184 Wood carving in the porch of Holy Trinity, Wonston, Sutton Scotney, Hants. 1909.

185 Inscription in Mission Hall, Walworth, in memory of CHARLES HERMAN PRIOR.
Full-size setting-out of inscription with rubbing on reverse; $10 \times 32\frac{3}{4}$; signed A. E. R. GILL, July 31, 1909.

186 Tablet St. John the Divine, Richmond, Surrey: WHOSOEVER
THOU ART THAT ENTEREST THIS CHURCH...
Rubbing; $11\frac{1}{4} \times 14\frac{3}{4}$; 1909.

187 Headstone in churchyard of St. Mary, Storrington, Sussex, with carving
of Chalice and Patten in low relief surmounting the inscription, in memory of
the Rev. GEORGE TYRRELL, d. July 1909.
Full-size drawing of inscription and chalice; signed A. E. R. Gill. Aug. '09.
Rubbing; 26×23; August 1909.

188 Tablet of incised letters (lettering in red) in St. Lawrence, Over Peover,
Knutsford, Cheshire, in memory of MICHAEL FARRELL, d. 1882 and of
his wife, d. 1869.
Pen and ink drawing (tinted), inscription in red; $3 \times 4\frac{1}{2}$; signed A. E. R. Gill,
Ditchling, Aug. '09.
Rubbing; $20 \times 24\frac{3}{4}$; unsigned and undated.

189 Memorial tablet for a window in St. Peter, Llanwenarth Citra, Govilon,
Abergavenny, in memory of HUGH BACKHOUSE CHURCH, d. 31
March 1909.
Full-size drawing; $17\frac{1}{2} \times 25\frac{1}{4}$; signed A. E. R. Gill, Ditchling, Sept. 1909.
Rubbing; $14\frac{1}{2} \times 23\frac{1}{2}$.

190 Inscription at King's College Hospital, Denmark Hill, London, S.E. 1909.
(See also Nos. 147, 182 and 269.)

191 Brass plate in memory of ROBERT CREIGHTON, d. 1878, his wife
and their children, commemorating the gift of windows in a church.
Pen and ink drawing (tinted); dated Oct. 18, 1909.
Rubbing; $21\frac{1}{4} \times 12\frac{1}{2}$.
[One of the children referred to was Mandell Creighton (1843–1901), Bishop
of Peterborough, 1891–97, and Bishop of London, 1897–1901.]

192 Inscription in relief for bust of JAMES MARTINEAU, 1805–1900.
Rubbing; $2\frac{1}{4} \times 14$; 1909.

193 Incised inscription: WHY MAKE YE THIS ADO ... AND WEEP
THE DAMSEL IS NOT DEAD...
Rubbing; $31 \times 48\frac{1}{2}$; unsigned and undated; c. 1909.

194 Hopton-Wood stone tablet in a chapel in St. Wulfran's Ovingdean near Brighton.

This commemorates the erection of the chapel, by Arthur Carey, of Downside, Roedean, in 1907.

This is on the foundation of a Norman Chantry which was destroyed by fire A.D. 1377.

Pen and ink scale drawings; $3\frac{1}{2} \times 6\frac{3}{4}$ and $3\frac{1}{2} \times 7\frac{1}{2}$; both signed A. E. R. Gill, Ditchling, Sussex and dated respectively, Nov. 15.09. and Nov. 16. 09.

Rubbing; 13×30; signed Eric Gill, 1909.

195 Stone tablet: NORTHEND for farm house at North Moreton, Didcot, occupied by the Boulter family in 1909.

Work executed *c.* 1909.

196 Inscription for reredos presented in memory of JOHN THOMAS ATKINSON, of Hillfield, Selby, Yorks., d. September 1909.

Rubbing; $3\frac{1}{2} \times 5$; [n.d.] *c.* 1909.

197 Tablet in St. Lawrence, Over Peover, Cheshire, in memory of ALFRED HERBERT WILLIAM FARRELL, d. 1909, and of his wife and children.

Pen and ink drawing (tinted), inscription in red; $5\frac{3}{4} \times 5\frac{1}{2}$; signed A. E. R. Gill, Ditchling, March, 1910.

Rubbing; 30×33; unsigned and undated.

198 Lettering for KEYMER & DISTRICT LAND CLUB.

This was done for the Club which used to meet at the 'Bull' Public house, Ditchling.

Work executed; *c.* 1910.

199 Headstone in memory of HOPE BROWN, wife of Alexander Easton Gibb of Kew & Rosyth, d. May 1909.

Rubbing of inscription; $12\frac{1}{2} \times 15\frac{3}{4}$; work executed April–June 1910.

200 Gravestone with inscription surmounted by a crucifix in Hopton-Wood stone, St. Egwin, Norton near Evesham, in memory of HANNAH MARIA BOULTER, d. 20 August 1909.

Pencil drawing (coloured); undated but signed A. E. R. Gill, Ditchling.

Work executed February–April 1910.

201 Foundation Stone for St. Jude-on-the-Hill, Garden Suburb, Hampstead, London, N.W., laid by the Hon. W. F. D. Smith, 25 April 1910.

Full-size setting-out; 19 × 33; March 1910.

[This work was commissioned by Sir Edwin Lutyens.]

202 Hopton-Wood stone tablet for the wall of a sea-side house. This represents a woman in a crouching position supporting the tablet which is inscribed in Greek characters: ΕΣΤΙΝ ΘΑΛΑΣΣΑ ΤΙΣ ΔΕ ΝΙΝ ΣΒΕΣΕΙ. ('There is the Sea, and who shall drain it dry?' *Agamemnon* of Aeschylus.)
Rubbing of inscription; $5\frac{1}{4} \times 7\frac{1}{4}$; 1910.

[One of E.G.'s earliest carvings. It was first exhibited at the Chenil Gallery, Chelsea, in January 1911.]

203 CRUCIFIXION. Hopton-Wood stone relief of a T-shaped Crucifix depicting a nude Christ, with the words NEC IN TIBIIS VERI BENE PLACITUM ERIT EI (Psalm 147.10) incised vertically upon the cross-shaft. On either side is inscribed in Greek caps. ΚΑΙΕΙΣΙΝ ΕΥΝΟΥΧΟΙ ΟΙΤΙΝΕΣ . . . (*And there be eunuchs . . .*) (S. Matthew, 19.12).
This was carved in 1910 and first exhibited at the Chenil Gallery, Chelsea, in January 1911. It was presented to the Tate Gallery by the Contemporary Art Society in 1920.
Dimensions: $37\frac{1}{4} \times 30\frac{3}{4}$.
(Cf. No. 203A.)

203A A ROLAND FOR AN OLIVER. Hopton-Wood stone relief of a panel depicting a nude female figure with words from Swinburne's *Hymn to Proserpine*: O PALE GALILEAN, BUT THESE THOU SHALT NOT TAKE: THE LAUREL THE PALM & THE PAEAN THE BREASTS OF THE NYMPHS IN THE BRAKE . . . inscribed round a rectangle.
This was carved in 1910 and first exhibited as a companion piece to the *Crucifixion* (q.v. No. 203) and exhibited at the Chenil Gallery, Chelsea, in January 1911. The title *A Roland for an Oliver* was that given to the work in the catalogue of the Exhibition. It was purchased by the Contemporary Art Society, to whom it still belongs, but is in the care of the Tate Gallery.
Rubbing; $37\frac{1}{4} \times 27\frac{1}{2}$; unsigned and undated.

[E.G. wrote to his brother Vernon, 'They are a pair—one being a symbol of renunciation and the other a symbol of acceptance.']

204 Tablet commemorating the gift of altar and ornaments in memory of ANNA FRANCES SPOONER, 1830–1906.
Rubbing; $11\frac{3}{4} \times 19\frac{1}{4}$; E.G., del., Joseph Cribb, sc.
Work executed *c.* 1910.

205 Monument at Haslemere with allegorical figure and inscription: IN MEMORIAM M.E.D[AKYNS] JAN III MCMVIII...
Sketch; $15\frac{1}{4} \times 9\frac{1}{2}$; 1910.
[Gill's drawing for this monument bears the following inscription: 'The body springs from the grave, the soul descends from an opening cloud; they rush together with inconceivable energy; they meet never again to part.' (Text to illustration in *Blake's Grave*, p. 82).]
Another sketch, showing a different design, a carving of Mother and Child set within a recess.
Sketch; $11\frac{1}{4} \times 8$; signed A.E.R.G. November 1910.

206 Letters: HEATHCOTE for a house designed by Sir Edwin Lutyens.
Sketch; $2 \times 16\frac{1}{4}$; and full-size setting-out of lettering; 4×32; both signed A. E. R. Gill. June 1910.

207 Foundation stone for house in Boys' Garden City, Woodford Green, Essex, laid in memory of Dr. THOMAS JOHN BARNARDO (1845–1905).
Drawing; $8\frac{3}{4} \times 17\frac{3}{4}$; signed A. E. R. Gill, July 1910.
(See also Nos. 208 and 209.)

208 Foundation stone for house in Boys' Garden City, Woodford Green, Essex, laid 21st July, 1910 in memory of KING EDWARD VII.
Drawing; $9 \times 17\frac{3}{4}$; signed A. E. R. Gill, July 1910.
(See also Nos. 207 and 209.)

209 Foundation stone for house in Boys' Garden City, Woodford Green, Essex, laid 21st July, 1910 in memory of Canon FLEMING.
Drawing; $8\frac{3}{4} \times 18$; July 1910.
(See also Nos. 207 and 208.)

210 Stone inscription in the passage-hall of house in Madingley Road, Cambridge, reading: FRANCIS DARWIN BUILT THIS HOUSE FOR FRANCIS & FRANCES CORNFORD 1910.
E.G. also carved the letters: CONDUIT HEAD on the beam of the porch of the front door of the same house.
Work executed August 1910.
(See also No. 371.)

211 Tablet inscribed: THE DOVES BINDERY / MDCCXCIII / THE DOVES PRESS / T.J. MCM C-S.

Sketch; signed A. E. R. Gill, Oct. 29/10.

Rubbing; $11\frac{7}{8} \times 22\frac{1}{4}$; signed Eric Gill, 1910.

[Established first as *The Doves Bindery* at 15 Upper Mall, Hammersmith, and later (*c.* 1908) at 1 The Terrace, Hammersmith, as *The Doves Press*, where it continued to flourish until 1916. The initials in the inscription relate to T. J. Cobden-Sanderson.]   [*See Plate VII*]

212 Tablet in Hopton-Wood stone commemorating the restoration of ST. ANDREW'S CHURCH, Tredunnoc, Usk, Mon., in 1910.
Full-size setting-out; $16\frac{1}{2} \times 18\frac{1}{4}$; *c.* 1910.

213 Foundation stone for Parish Hall, St. John the Divine, Richmond, Surrey, laid by Viscount Halifax, 10 February 1911.
Rubbing; $11\frac{1}{2} \times 22\frac{3}{4}$; signed E.G. del., J.C. sc. November 1910.

214 Inscription on headstone at Worthing, Sussex, in memory of CECIL EDGAR FISH, d. 1910.
There are three pencil drawings (tinted) for different designs, all signed E. Gill, Ditchling, Sussex, Nov. 1910.
Rubbing of portion of inscription; $11\frac{1}{2} \times 27$; endorsed by E.G. 'by Joseph Cribb 1911'.

215 Exhibition piece. Inscription on Hopton-Wood stone, $10\frac{3}{4} \times 19\frac{1}{2}$, cut in 1910.
IF IT IS MORE BLESSED / TO GIVE THAN TO RECEIVE / IT IS MORE BLESSED TO / RECEIVE THAN TO REJECT
[This was exhibited and sold at the Alpine Club Gallery, May 1918. Now in the collection of Ernest W. Porter, Derby.]

216 Inscription in memory of MARJORIE STEELE, d. January 1910.
Rubbing; $18\frac{1}{2} \times 15$; [n.d.] *c.* 1910.

217 Inscription (from Goethe) on marble: OB NICHT NATUR / ZULETZT SICH / DOCH ERGRUNDE the letters painted red.
Size of tablet: $6 \times 14\frac{1}{2}$.
Stylistic evidence suggests that this was cut *c.* 1910.
[Presented to the late Edward Johnston at Ditchling it is now in the collection of Evan R. Gill. A free translation might run: 'Perhaps Nature may at last reveal her secrets'.]

218 Inscription in memory of General Sir HENRY ERRINGTON LONGDEN K.C.B., C.S.L.—1819–1890. Died at Bournemouth, January 1890.
Rubbing; 22 × 31¼; [n.d.] *c.* 1910.

219 Altar tomb in St. Mary's Roman Catholic Cemetery, Kensal Green, London, in memory of FRANCIS THOMPSON, 1859–1907. This inscription is on the foot of the tombstone and is followed by a line from the poet's *To my Godchild* LOOK FOR ME IN THE NURSERIES OF HEAVEN.
Drawings; signed Eric Gill. Ditchling, Feb. 4, 1911.
Rubbing of inscription; 17½ × 17½; signed E.G. March 1911.
(See also No. 243.)

220 Stone laid by His Majesty King Edward the Seventh, 27 June 1908. This stone is over the central door of King Edward VII's Gallery, British Museum extension, Russell Street, Bloomsbury, London.
Sketch (1 in. scale); 3 × 11¾; signed Eric Gill, April 1911.
(See also No. 394.)

221 Ledger stone with inscription and Coat of Arms, in the crypt, St. Paul's Cathedral, London, in memory of WILLIAM HOLMAN HUNT, O.M., Painter, 1827–1910.
Pencil drawing, numbered '1'; signed E.G. 29.5.11.
Four alternative designs were submitted, one (Coat of Arms) is signed E.G. July 7'11.
Full-size layout of portion of inscription; 9½ × 23.
Rubbing of inscription; 33 × 23¼; unsigned and undated.
Work executed 1911.

222 Headstone of Portland stone in the Extra Mural Cemetery, Brighton, in memory of SIR THOMAS EKINS FULLER K.C.M.G. 1831–1910.
Two pencil scale drawings (coloured); signed Eric Gill, 30 May 11 & 29 June 1911.
Full-size detail of moulding; signed E.G. 23 Aug. 1911.
Rubbing of inscription; 20 × 24.

223 Memorial cross, Wykeham Abbey, Scarborough, in memory of CECILIA MARY CHARLOTTE DOWNE, 1838–1910, wife of Hugh Richard, 8th Viscount Downe.
Full-size details; 83½ × 24; signed Eric Gill, Ditchling, Sussex, July 4, 1911.

224 Brass plate in Canterbury Cathedral recording the recovery and replacement of ancient glass, in memory of ANNIE MOORE, d. December 1906.
Pencil drawing, full-size; $4\frac{1}{2} \times 18$.
Rubbing; $4\frac{1}{2} \times 18$; June 1911.

225 Foundation stone for the Psychological Laboratory, Cambridge, laid 18 July 1911 by Esther, wife of WOLF MYERS in whose memory the greater part of the building was provided by his family and friends.
Full-size setting-out of lettering; 22×18; signed Eric Gill. June 27, 1911.
Rubbing; $20\frac{1}{2} \times 17\frac{1}{2}$; endorsed: 'Supposed to be a copy of my drawing! A very decent piece of lettering but scarcely like the copy. E.G.'

226 Bronze sundial on pedestal of grey Roman stone, with inscriptions on all four sides, in the churchyard St. Margaret, Ditchling. Erected to commemorate the Coronation of King George V.
Pencil drawings (tinted); signed Eric Gill, Ditchling, Sussex. June 28. & 30, 1911.
Rubbing of portion of inscription on one of the sides; $15 \times 6\frac{3}{4}$.
Lettering cut by Joseph Cribb.

227 Inscription for beams: BUILT AT THE INSTANCE OF H. T. ANGELL.
Full-size detail of lettering; signed Eric Gill. 9 March 1911.

228 Headstone of Hopton-Wood stone in Kenilworth Churchyard in memory of EDWARD HERBERT DRAPER 1841–1911. Clerk to the Guild or Fraternity of the Body of Christ of the Skinners of the City of London.
Pencil drawings (tinted); signed E.G. 24 July 1911 and September 3, 1911.
Rubbing of inscription; 22×22; Jan. 1912; endorsed by E.G. 'H.J.C., Ditchling, Jan, 1912.'

229 Incised tablet of Hopton-Wood stone in Hampstead in memory of OSCAR GUTTMANN, d. August 1910.
Pencil drawing (coloured); signed Eric Gill, Ditchling, Sx. 3 & 9 Sept. 1911.
Rubbing; $23\frac{3}{4} \times 14\frac{3}{4}$; September 1911.

230 Portland headstone surmounted by a cross within foliage, St. John the Evangelist, Holdenhurst, Bournemouth, Hants., in memory of GERALD PEEL 1847–1910.
Drawing (tinted); signed Eric Gill, Ditchling, Sx. September 7 1911.

31

D

Alternative and accepted design—drawing (tinted) 1 in. scale; signed Eric Gill, Ditchling, Sx. Sept. 14. '11.

Rubbing of inscription; 20 × 26; unsigned and undated.

Dimensions of headstone: 54 × 27.

Work executed by Joseph Cribb.

231 Anagram inscription and emblem incised on Hopton-Wood stone: ΙΧΘΥΕ.
Rubbing; $7\frac{1}{4} \times 7\frac{3}{4}$; [n.d.] c. 1911.

232 Headstone of Portland stone in churchyard St. Simon & St. Jude, East Dean, Eastbourne, in memory of ANTHONY GEORGE NEW, 1870–1911.
Rubbing; $21 \times 16\frac{3}{4}$; signed Eric Gill, Ditchling, Sx. 1912.

233 Bronze tablet within a marble frame on South side of Chapel of Bailliol College, Oxford, in memory of EDWARD CAIRD, 1835–1908.
Tablet; $32\frac{5}{8} \times 25\frac{1}{4}$.
Pencil drawing (coloured) $\frac{1}{4}$ full-size; signed Eric Gill. Oct. 10, 1911.

234 Gravestone in St. Mary's, Teddington, in memory of STEPHEN HALES, D.D., F.R.S., Clerk of the Closet to the Princess of Wales, Minister of St. Mary's Teddington, for 51 years, d. January 1761.
Rubbing of inscription; $19\frac{1}{4} \times 28$; signed Eric Gill, Nov. 1911.
[This stone, the gift of certain botanists, replaces one that had become partly obliterated. There is also a monument to him in Westminster Abbey.]

235 Gravestone in churchyard of St. George's, West Grinstead, Horsham, Sussex, in memory of ISABELLA MARY COWIE, 1846–1903, also of ELLEN COWIE, 1851–1906.
Full-size sketch of portion of inscription; $10 \times 28\frac{1}{2}$; signed Eric Gill, Ditchling Sussex, December 4 1911.
Rubbing of inscriptions; $21\frac{1}{2} \times 28\frac{1}{2}$; signed H.J.C. December 1911.

236 Gravestone of Hopton-Wood stone in Brookwood Cemetery, Woking, in memory of LINDSEY FORSTER BATTEN d. 1865 and NORMAN GOTTFRIED BATTEN, d. 1873.
Full-size setting-out; $9\frac{1}{4} \times 23\frac{3}{4}$; signed Eric Gill, Ditchling, Sussex, 28 December 1911.
Rubbings; $9 \times 23\frac{1}{2}$.

237 Inscription in Greek, set out in an ellipse: ΑΡΙΣΤΟΣ. ΙΑΤΡΟΣ ΚΑΙ ΦΙΛΟΣΟΦΟΣ ('An excellent doctor and philosopher').
Rubbing; $12\frac{3}{4} \times 15\frac{3}{4}$; c. 1911.

238 Headstone in Barn Hill Cemetery, Broughty Ferry, Dundee, in memory of JOHN OGILVIE of Westlands, Broughty Ferry, 1831–1911.
Pencil drawing (coloured); signed Eric Gill, Ditchling, Sx. 14.2.12.

239 Tablet of Hopton-Wood stone in Teffont Ewyas Church, Salisbury, in memory of ELLEN FLORA KEATINGE, Lady of the Manor of Teffont-Ewyas, d. 1907. Also of MAURICE KEATINGE, d. 1896.
Pencil drawing ⅛ f-s. dated 15 Feb. 1912.
Rubbing of inscription; 34¾ × 21½.

240 A four-line inscription incised 1¾ in. roman capital letters: MAKE THEM TO BE NUMBERED WITH THY SAINTS.
Rubbing; 15½ × 17½; unsigned and undated; c. 1912.

241 Tablet of Hopton-Wood stone in Teffont-Ewyas Church, Salisbury, in memory of MARGARET HELEN MAYNE, d. 1905 and was buried beneath the tower of this church.
Rubbing; 12 × 25½; March 1912.

242 Inscription on top of a sundial of Portland stone for Neil Lyons, at Wivelsfield, Sussex: FULL MANY A GLORIOUS MORNING HAVE I SEEN.
Rubbing; 11¾ × 12; March 1912.

243 Memorial tablet of Hopton-Wood stone in Manchester University, in memory of FRANCIS THOMPSON, Poet. 1859–1907. Student of Owens College 1877–1884.
Pencil drawing ⅛ f-s.; signed E.G. 20.3.12.
F-s. details; signed E.G. 28.3.12.
(See also No. 219.)

244 Cross of Green Borrowdale stone in memory of ISABELLA, widow of John Elliott Huxtable, died December 1909.
There are no less than five careful pencil drawings (coloured) for this work and a full-size sketch (outline only) of the cross signed Eric Gill 30.3.12 (Revised 2 May 12).
Rubbing of letters and sculptured emblems of fish and K̵; 27½ × 8; undated. Work executed April–May 1912. Location unknown.

245 Brass plate for clock in the church tower, St. James the Great, Silsoe, Bedford, commemorating the visit of King Edward VII, 25 July 1909.

Pen and ink drawing, $\frac{1}{4}$ full-size; $4\frac{3}{4} \times 3\frac{1}{4}$; signed Eric Gill, Ditchling, Sussex, 24.4.12.

Full-size setting-out; $20\frac{1}{4} \times 13\frac{1}{4}$; signed Eric Gill, Ditchling, Sussex, 16.5.12.

Rubbing; $20\frac{1}{4} \times 13\frac{1}{4}$; endorsed 'engraved by C. Mylam, 1912'.

246 Cruciform headstone and foot-stone of Portland stone in Keymer Cemetery, Sussex, in memory of FREDERICK THOMAS RICHARD WHITE—1896–1911.

Pencil sketches, with measurements, also key drawings, full-size, of section; from E.G.'s hand, but neither signed nor dated.

Pencil drawing (coloured); scale $1\frac{1}{2}$ in.; signed Eric Gill, Ditchling, Sx. May 6 1912.

Rubbing of lettering; $13\frac{3}{4} \times 18$; unsigned and undated.

247 Stone tablet in Prefect's room, Godolphin School, Salisbury, commemorating the gift, by past & present pupils and their mistresses, of a museum to honour the memory of ETHEL EMMELINE JONES and her twenty-one years of service to the school. September 30, 1911.

Actual size: $11 \times 27\frac{1}{2}$.

Full-size setting-out; signed Eric Gill 15 June 1912.

Rubbing; endorsed 'Cut by H. J. Cribb 1911 [sic] (for Eric Gill).'

248 Portland stone tablet in Barn Hill Cemetery, Broughty Ferry, Dundee, in memory of GEORGE OGILVIE. 1851–1912.

Sketch $\frac{1}{8}$ full-size; signed E.G. 17.6.12.

Rubbing of inscription; $12\frac{1}{2} \times 22$.

249 Headstone in Green Honister slate at Rickerby, near Carlisle, in memory of PRISCILLA HANNAH JOHNSTON, d. January 1912.

Half full-size sketch; signed Eric Gill, 8 July 1912.

Rubbing of inscription; $25\frac{3}{4} \times 31\frac{1}{4}$.

250 Headstone of Hopton-Wood stone in churchyard of St. Egwin's, Norton, Evesham, in memory of WALTER CONSITT BOULTER, 1848–1912.

Pencil drawing (coloured); signed Eric Gill, Ditchling, Sx. 26 July 1912.

Rubbing; $15 \times 13\frac{1}{2}$; endorsed 'By H. J. Cribb for Eric Gill, 1913.'

251 Headstone of Hopton-Wood stone in Bradford Cemetery in memory of BERTHA, wife of Moritz Rothenstein, 1844–1912.

Three pencil drawings (coloured); signed Eric Gill, Ditchling, Sx. Oct. 4 1912.

Rubbing; $12\frac{1}{4} \times 16\frac{1}{4}$; signed Eric Gill, 1912.
Additional inscription commemorating MORITZ ROTHENSTEIN, born December 1836 died December 1914.
Rubbing; $9\frac{3}{4} \times 16\frac{1}{4}$; unsigned and undated.

252 Tablet of light Hopton-Wood stone in St. Andrew's, Steyning, Sussex, recording the removal of galleries, etc., in memory of ARTHUR CON-GREVE PRIDGEON, vicar, 1882–1907.
Full-size setting-out; $17 \times 27\frac{1}{2}$; signed Eric Gill, 7 Aug. 1912.
Rubbing; $14\frac{1}{4} \times 27\frac{1}{2}$; endorsed 'cut by Eric Gill, Ditchling, Sx. 1912'.

253 Gravestone of Stancliffe stone in memory of SYBIL GWENDOLINE SPENDER CLAY, d. March 1912.
Full-size sketch; $16\frac{1}{2} \times 18\frac{1}{2}$; signed Eric Gill, Aug. 19.1912.
Rubbing; $18\frac{3}{4} \times 14$.

254 Tablet of white marble with leaded letters, in a niche at Manchester Crematorium (Southern Cemetery), in memory of JOHN TREGO GILL, 1847–1912.
Drawing of portion of inscription.
Rubbing; $8\frac{1}{4} \times 15\frac{1}{4}$.
Letters cut by Joseph Cribb, October 1912.
[John Trego Gill was E.G.'s uncle.]

255 Tomb in memory of OSCAR WILDE, in Père Lachaise Cemetery, Paris, carved by Jacob Epstein with inscription by E.G.
Size of inscription, which is on the middle stone of the back of the memorial: 40×56.
Three pencil drawings; signed Eric Gill, 17.20. & 22. Sept., 1912.
Inscription cut by Joseph Cribb.

256 Hopton-Wood stone tablet placed by the Ancient Order of Druids at Southdown Lodge, Hassocks, Sussex, to commemorate the planting of a tree to mark the Coronation of King George V, 22 June, 1911.
Rubbing; $9\frac{3}{4} \times 20$; cut by Joseph Cribb, November 1912.

257 Cross in churchyard of St. Nicholas, Guildford, in memory of SYDNEY MELVILLE, widow of Joseph Spender Clay, wife of Beresford V. Melville, d. May 1912.
Quarter-size drawing: $11\frac{1}{4} \times 9\frac{1}{2}$; signed Eric Gill, 14 Nov. '12.

258 Wall tablet for WORTH MANOR HOUSE, Worth, nr. Crawley, Sussex, the home of Wilfrid Scawen Blunt. The tablet records the names of the builders, carpenters and labourers, etc.
Rubbing; $35\frac{1}{4} \times 23\frac{1}{2}$; endorsed 'Cut by H. J. Cribb for Eric Gill. 1912.'

259 Tablet of Hopton-Wood stone in St. Mary's School, Ealing, in memory of Dame JANE RAWLINSON, who founded and endowed the school in 1712.
Half f-s. sketch; $11\frac{1}{2} \times 12\frac{1}{2}$; signed Eric Gill, 4 Dec. '12.
Rubbing; $22\frac{1}{2} \times 24\frac{1}{2}$.

260 Memorial of light Hopton-Wood stone in St. Nicholas, Cranleigh, Surrey, in memory of AMY BONHAM, d. 1910, with inscription from *Morte d'Arthur*: I TRUST I DO NOT DISPLEASE GOD. FOR WHEN I REMEMBER OF THE BEAUTY AND OF THE NOBLESSE . . .
This followed by: HER MOTHER and Feb. 18, 1910.
Full-size setting-out; $10\frac{3}{4} \times 23\frac{3}{4}$; signed Eric Gill, 6 Dec. 1912.
Rubbing; $8\frac{1}{2} \times 19\frac{1}{4}$.

261 Inscriptions on the stone base of bronze statue in the People's Park, West Cliff, Whitby, Yorks. (the work of John Tweed) in memory of Captain JOHN COOK, R.N., 1728–1779.
Drawing, half full-size; front: $7\frac{1}{4} \times 14\frac{1}{2}$; left side: 12×9; right side: $3\frac{1}{2} \times 9$.
The above on one sheet signed Eric Gill, Ditchling, Sussex 13.12.12.
Rubbing; of front: $10\frac{1}{2} \times 28\frac{3}{4}$; of left side: $28 \times 17\frac{1}{2}$; of right side: $8\frac{1}{2} \times 17$.

262 Incised tablet, with inscription in Latin, in St. John's, Richmond, Surrey, in memory of MAUD WITHERS, d. 1911.
Rubbing; $11 \times 12\frac{1}{4}$; endorsed 'cut by H. J. Cribb for Eric Gill. 1912'.

263 Incised inscription on base of statue of the Blessed Virgin: TU AD LIBERANDUM SUSCEPTURUS HOMINEM NON HORRUISTI VIRGINIS UTERUM.
Rubbing of inscription; $14\frac{1}{4} \times 16\frac{1}{2}$; signed Eric Gill 1912.

264 Marble Sepulchral urn at Golders Green Crematorium in memory of ELBERT JAN VAN WISSELINGH, 1848–1912.
Full-size drawing; $8\frac{1}{2} \times 13\frac{3}{4}$; signed Eric Gill, Ditchling, Sussex. 27 Jan. 1913.
Rubbing of inscription; $5 \times 9\frac{3}{4}$.

265 Brass plate in the Nicholson ward of Children's Hospital, Brighton, in memory of Major S. Nicholson. 27 August 1912.
Full-size setting-out; $8\frac{1}{2} \times 38\frac{1}{4}$; signed Eric Gill, Ditchling, Sussex, 5 March 1913.
Rubbing; $8\frac{1}{2} \times 38\frac{1}{4}$; March 1913.

266 Hopton-Wood stone tablet, Holy Trinity, Sloane Street, London, recording the gift of the reredos (the work of John Tweed) in memory of JOHN ROSS, 1859–1905.
Pencil drawing; 22 March 1913.
Rubbing; $26\frac{1}{4} \times 35\frac{1}{2}$; endorsed 'Cut by Joseph Cribb for Eric Gill, April–May, 1913.'
[This tablet is to be found on the back of the reredos which was unveiled Trinity Sunday, 2 June 1912.]

267 Tomb of Portland stone in the churchyard, St. Mary the Virgin, Calne, Wilts., in memory of Sir CHARLES HENRY STUART RICH, 4th Baronet of Shirley, d. January 1913.
Drawings, $\frac{1}{8}$ full-size; May 1913.

268 Headstone in churchyard of St. Nicholas, Sevenoaks, Kent, in memory of CHARLES HERBERT AYLWIN, d. 1909, and of his daughter KATH-LEEN MABEL GRACE MOORE. d. 1911.
Full-size drawing for additional inscription; signed E.G. 27.6.13.
Rubbing; $11\frac{1}{2} \times 22$; June 1913.

269 King's College Hospital, Denmark Hill, London, S.E.
(a) Letters for Ward floors, full size; 6×128; signed Eric Gill, Ditchling, Sussex, 21.6.13.
(b) Lettering on floors at entrance to Wards. Rough setting-out—full-size; $14\frac{1}{2} \times 69\frac{1}{2}$; signed Eric Gill, June 2 1913.
(c) Lettering to entrances $\frac{1}{8}$ full-size; signed Eric Gill, 18.7.14.
(d) Inscription recording opening of hospital by King George V. July 26 1913.
Rubbing of inscription; unsigned and undated; $22 \times 24\frac{1}{2}$.
(See also Nos. 147, 182 and 190.)

270 Gravestone with kerbing in Ditchling churchyard, in memory of RICHARD LINGARD STOKES, d. February 1912.
Pencil drawing (coloured); signed Eric Gill, Sopers, Ditchling. 14.2.12.
Rubbing of lettering on kerb; 17×52; endorsed 'S. Geering for Eric Gill, Ditchling, Sussex, Sept–Oct. 1913'.

271 Holy Water stoups of polished Hopton-Wood stone with inscriptions
IN NOMINE PATRIS...
These were commissioned by Wilfred Meynell.
There are three drawings; all signed E. G. The first dated 1 Aug. 1913, the
other two dated Aug. 21 '13, together with rubbings of five different designs
or layouts.

272 Incised inscription (letters in red) on tablet in the Deaf & Dumb Institute,
Kemp Town, Brighton: BOYS' RECREATION ROOM HUGH S.
HEAL MEMORIAL 1913.
Pencil drawing by E.G.; unsigned and undated.
Rubbing; $11\frac{1}{2} \times 19\frac{1}{2}$; signed Cribb 30 September 1913.

273 Tablet inscribed: OMNIA PER IPSUM ET SINE IPSO NIHIL.
Size of tablet: $5\frac{3}{4} \times 8\frac{3}{4}$.
[This tablet was cut in September 1913 and given by Eric Gill to his father for his
birthday, 30 September 1913. It is now at St. Mary's House, Buxted, Sussex.]

273A Lines from Tennyson's *The Lotus Eaters*: LET THERE BE MUSIC
HERE ... for a panel over the fire-place in the music room at Leasam House,
Playden, Rye, Sussex. With floral emblems (coloured) executed by E.G.'s
brother Macdonald Gill. 1914.
This was commissioned by Lady Maud Warrender who lived there. The house
was subsequently sold to the Sussex County Council in 1946.
Pencil drawing of inscription; $1\frac{3}{4} \times 7\frac{1}{2}$ ($\frac{1}{8}$ f-s.). (Dimensions of panel, $19\frac{1}{2} \times$
$66\frac{1}{2}$); endorsed by E.G. 'Please return to Eric Gill, Ditchling, Sx. Sept. 1913'.

273B Headstone of Portland stone at Birchington, Kent, in memory of
BRIAN CHAMBREY TOWNSHEND—1874–1913.
Pencil drawing; signed Eric Gill, Oct. 2. 13.
Rubbing of portion of the inscription; 37×30; February 1914.

274 Wall tablet of Hopton-Wood stone in the Children's Hospital, Brighton,
for the LOUISE SASSOON ELECTRICAL & X RAY DEPART-
MENT.
Quarter full-size sketch; signed E.G. 29.10.13.
Rubbing; $13\frac{3}{4} \times 31\frac{1}{2}$; endorsed 'H. J. Cribb for E.G. Nov. 1913.'

275 Ledgerstone at Howden, nr. Selby, Yorks., in memory of ROBERT
STANLEY SCHOLFIELD—1841–1913.
Rubbing; $20\frac{1}{2} \times 29$; signed Geering for E.G. November 1913.

276 Stone tablet on the Gyde Almshouses, Painswick, Glos., inscribed: THESE ALMS HOUSES WERE BUILT AND ENDOWED BY EDWIN FRANCIS GYDE 1913.
Work executed November 1913.

277 Tablet of white marble, with green marble border, in memory of JAMES FRANCIS HATFIELD-HARTER, d. 1910.
Pencil drawing; $\frac{1}{4}$ full-size; dated 3 Dec. 1913.
Full-size drawing; $12\frac{1}{2} \times 11\frac{1}{4}$; signed Eric Gill, 19.1.14.
Rubbing; $11\frac{1}{4} \times 10$.
Letters cut by Joseph Cribb.

278 Stone tablet on north wall of the Chancel, Jesus College Chapel, Cambridge, with inscription in Latin, in memory of HENRY ARTHUR MORGAN, D.D., who served the College for 63 years as Student, Fellow, Tutor and Master. Died 3 September 1912.
Pencil sketch $\frac{1}{8}$ full-size; signed E.G. Ditchling, Sx., 21 Nov. 1913.
Full-size detail of portion of inscription, in pen and ink; signed Eric Gill, Ditchling, Sx. 28 Nov. 1913.
(See also No. 562A.)

278A Incised letters REGIUS PROFESSOR OF PHYSIC and LIBRARY.
Rubbing of first inscription; $13\frac{1}{2} \times 24\frac{1}{2}$; endorsed 'Cambridge Nov. 1915. H.J.C.'.
[For Cambridge University.]

279 Stone tablet for Open-Air wards for . . . Hospital erected and endowed in 1913 by Samuel Bythesea and his wife.
Rubbing; $19\frac{1}{2} \times 35$; December 1913.

280 Headstone of Portland stone in churchyard of St. Giles', Packwood, Hockley Heath, Warwick, in memory of LUCY JANE COUCHMAN, d. June 4 1913. aged 57 years.
Drawing; $21\frac{1}{2} \times 17\frac{1}{2}$; signed H. J. Cribb for Eric Gill (Dec. 1913).
Work executed April 1914.

281 Tablet of White Cicilian marble commemorating the Silver Wedding of HERBERT WILLIAM CRIBB and ALICE MARY CRIBB, 1888–1913.
Rubbing; $10 \times 12\frac{1}{2}$; [n.d.] c. 1913.
[The parents of Joseph and Laurie Cribb, E.G.'s assistants for many years.]

282 Tablet in Lincoln Cathedral in memory of WILLIAM O'NEILL, M.D., C.M., M.R.C.P, London, 1830–1905.
Rubbing; 23 × 25; endorsed 'Cut by H. J. Cribb for Eric Gill. 1913'.

283 Wall tablet, incised inscription, in English and Latin: I AM THE FLOWER OF THE FIELD AND THE LILY OF THE VALLEYS. and: EGO FLOS CAMPI ET . . .
Rubbing; 30 × 20; endorsed 'Cut by S. Geering (for Eric Gill). 1913'.
[This was cut for Exhibition purposes.]

284 The fourteen Stations of the Cross carved in low relief on Hopton-Wood stone, in Westminster Cathedral, London. The titles are in English; texts in Latin.
Actual size; 68 × 68.
The work was executed 1914–18.
F-s. detail of mouldings, etc., of individual panels, and amongst others drawings dated 24 April 1914, signed either Eric Gill or E.G. These drawings are now in the Victoria & Albert Museum.
Rubbings of inscriptions for titles; 8 × 67.
[Let into the floor, beneath the 14th Station, is a tablet cut by Laurie Cribb: E.G. LAPIDARIUS 1882–1940.]

284A Stone tablet, letters incised: OUR FATHER WHO ART IN HEAVEN . . .
The Lord's Prayer; English and Latin in alternate lines.
Rubbing; 13¾ × 35½; endorsed 'W. T. Geering for E.G. Ditchling Common. March 1914.'
[This was cut for exhibition purposes.]

285 Inscription: MARY COOKE. 1839–1913.
Rubbing; 4½ × 14¼; signed H.J.C. for E.G. 9.3.1914.

286 KING'S COLLEGE FOR WOMEN, Campden Hill, London, W.
(a) Foundation Stone of Hopton-Wood stone, for Queen Mary's Hostel, laid by H.R.H. Princess Christian, 11 June 1914.
Rubbing; 22 × 36.
(b) Full-size details; signed Eric Gill, Ditchling Common, Sx. 14.4.14.
(c) Nine templates for 12 in. letters for laboratories; June 1915.

287 Granite Cross at Upton-on-Severn, Worcs., in memory of GEORGE EDWARD MARTIN, 1829–1905, and MARIA HENRIETTA his wife, 1839–1912.

F-s. drawing for inscription; $19\frac{3}{4} \times 39\frac{1}{2}$; signed Eric Gill. Ap.4,1914. (See also No. 87a.)

288 Inscription on Hopton-Wood stone for lamp and niche: LUMEN AD REVELATIONEM GENTIUM.
Full-size drawing and rubbing; signed Eric Gill, Ladyday 1914.

288A Incised lettering on oak board THE DECOY for the lintel of Joseph Thorp's 'Decoy Press' at Poling, Sussex.
Pencil sketch, full-size; $2\frac{5}{8} \times 11$; signed E.G. 14.4.14.

289 Portland headstone in Bisham churchyard, Berks., in memory of MALCOLM CORRIE POWELL, 1863–1913.
Pencil sketch, tinted; signed Eric Gill, Ditchling Common, Sx. 16.4.14.
Size of headstone: 39×24.

290 Pillar sundial at Newnham College, Cambridge, in memory of the princi-palship of ELEANOR MILDRED SIDGWICK, 1892–1911.
Full-size drawing of inscription; $17\frac{1}{2} \times 17$; signed Eric Gill, 16.4.14.
Rubbing; $17\frac{1}{2} \times 17$.

291 Brass Plate commemorating the gift of windows by Mary Ellen Creighton in memory of JANE CREIGHTON.
Drawing, full-size; $4\frac{1}{4} \times 14\frac{1}{2}$; signed Eric Gill, Ditchling Common, Sussex. May 6, 1914.

292 Inscription of about 70 letters in Latin capitals on Hornton stone in memory of OWEN LITTLE, cut by Joseph Cribb, May 1914.

293 Tablet of Hopton-Wood stone in memory of WINIFRED MARION SLATER—1876–1914. Headmistress of . . . School September 1907 to March 1914.
Pencil drawing (tinted); by E.G. unsigned but dated 18.5.14.
Rubbing; 18×35, May 1914.

294 Lettering: GUNNERY and NAVIGATION cut on the bases of two statues in the new arch, Buckingham Palace. June 1914.

295 Headstone of Portland stone in Bell's Hill Cemetery, Barnet, in memory of JOSEPH FRANK PAYNE—1840–1910.
Pencil drawing (coloured); signed Eric Gill, Ditchling Common, Sx. June 12 1914.
Rubbing of inscription; $13\frac{1}{2} \times 22$.
An additional inscription was cut in 1932.

296 White marble tablet for Mortuary Chapel at Richmond, Surrey, erected by Constance and William Sandover in memory of their Mothers, SUSANNAH ATHERTON of Richmond and MARY SANDOVER of Adelaide, Australia. 1914.
Rubbing of inscription; $17\frac{1}{4} \times 52\frac{1}{2}$; endorsed 'By H. J. Cribb for E.G.' September 1914.

297 Tablet of Hopton-Wood stone in memory of ALEXANDER NIGEL TROTTER, Lieut. 3rd Battn. The Royal Scots, 1894–1914.
Rubbing: $10\frac{3}{4} \times 29\frac{3}{4}$; January 1915.
Letters cut by Joseph Cribb.

298 Headstone and kerbing of Portland stone at Hampstead in memory of . . . CALDERON. October 1914.

299 Two-line inscription on base of statue: THE BURGHERS OF CALAIS—AUGUSTE RODIN in The Victoria Tower Gardens, Westminster.
Actual size of inscription 60×8.
Letters cut by Joseph Cribb, from drawings by E.G., October 1914.

300 Inscription on panel for Norman & Burt, Brighton: WEIGHT SHOULD NOT BE PLACED . . .
Rubbing; $5\frac{1}{2} \times 14\frac{1}{2}$; endorsed H.J.C[ribb] for E.G. Nov. 1914.

301 Memorial Cross in English oak with bronze tablet (probably at Walton Heath) in memory of HERBERT EDGAR REID of 'The Oaks' Walton Heath, d. April 1914.
Full-size setting-out of inscription; $19\frac{1}{2} \times 7\frac{1}{4}$; signed Eric Gill for E. W. Gimson. 30 December 1914.

302 Hopton-Wood stone tablet in Manchester University in memory of GEORGE ROBERT GISSING, 1857–1903, A student of Owens College, 1872–1876.
Pencil sketch, $\frac{1}{8}$ f-s.; signed E.G. Dec. 3 '14.
Full-size layout of letters white on black ground; endorsed 'H. J. Cribb for Eric Gill, September 1914'.
Rubbing; 10×23; signed H. J. Cribb for Eric Gill, September 1914.

303 Inscription commemorating the restoration and enlargement of church room, St. Mary the Virgin, Primrose Hill, London, in memory of the Reverend A. SPENCER, c. 1913.

Rubbing; $23\frac{1}{2} \times 36$.
Work executed *c.* 1914.

304 Tablet inscribed: INSTAR AMORIS ERAT NVNC AVREVS INTER AMORES ACCIPITVR CAESPES PRAETEGIT OSSA CANIS. MCMXIV.
Rubbing; $4\frac{1}{2} \times 13\frac{1}{4}$; [n.d.] *c.* 1914.

305 Inscription: OPERA MANUUM NOSTRARUM DIRIGE SUPER NOS: ET OPUS MANUUM NOSTRARUM DIRIGE.
Rubbing; $9\frac{1}{4} \times 18$; signed Geering (& E.G.) Feb. 1915.

306 Incised inscription, in Latin, on building in Scarborough recording damage by German shell-fire in 1914 and its restoration in 1915: HOC AEDIFICIUM TORMENTIS HOSTIUM VERBERATUM GER-MANORUM BARBARIAM TESTATUR . . .
Rubbing; $17\frac{1}{2} \times 53\frac{1}{2}$; cut by Joseph Cribb, February 1915.

307 Incised inscription in memory of MARY HAMILTON widow of John Hamilton of Brownhall & St. Ermans Island, Co. Donegal.
Rubbing; $16\frac{1}{4} \times 24\frac{1}{2}$; signed H. J. Cribb, Spring 1915.

308 Carving and lettering of panels for font St. Joseph's (R.C.) Church, Pickering, Yorks.
Two full-size drawings of details; signed 'E.G, 28.8.15' and 'Eric Gill 3 Dec. 1915', respectively.
[The carving of the panels occupied E.G. and Joseph Cribb on various dates to March 1916.]

309 Inscription of 191 2 in. incised letters and thirty-five 3 in. raised letters on pedestal of monument in Lincoln Cathedral in memory of EDWARD KING—1829–1910, Bishop of Lincoln 1885–1910.
Drawing, $\frac{1}{8}$ full-size; signed Eric Gill, 19 June 1915.
There are three rubbings of portions of the inscription.

310 Roll of Honour on oak tablet, commemorating those members of the staff of John Eede Butt & Sons, Littlehampton, who gave their lives in the Great War 1914–1918.
Full-size detail; signed Eric Gill 9 July 1915.
Rubbing of inscription; $30\frac{1}{2} \times 21$.

311 Gravestone with Cross and kerbing of Hopton-Wood stone, St. Mary, Bayford, Hertford, in memory of HARRIET C. HORNBY, 1840–1915.

Pencil and wash drawing; signed Eric Gill, Ditchling Common, Sussex, 14 July 1915.

Rubbing; $13\frac{1}{2} \times 25$; signed E.G. del., J. Cribb, sc. November 1915.

312 Mural tablet in St. Mary & St. Nicholas, Trumpington, Cambridge, in memory of FRANCIS PERCY CAMPBELL PEMBERTON, Captain 2nd Life Guards, killed in action 19 October 1914, aged 29.

Pencil drawing (tinted); $\frac{1}{8}$ f-s.; dated 14 July 1915.

Rubbing of inscription; $29\frac{1}{2} \times 19\frac{1}{4}$; endorsed 'H.J. C[ribb] for E.G., Oct. 1915' and signed E.G. 6.10.15.

313 Headstone of Hopton-Wood stone at Broughty Ferry, Dundee, in memory of JOHN EDMOND GORDON—1864–1914.

Pencil sketch by E.G. but neither signed nor dated.

Letters cut by H. J. Cribb, August 1915.

314 Hopton-Wood stone tablet, the inscription surmounted by a Coat of Arms, in St. Mary the Virgin, Stratfieldsaye, Reading, in memory of Lord RICHARD WELLESLEY, Captain, 1st Battn. Grenadier Guards, 2nd son of Arthur, 4th Duke of Wellington, killed in action 29th October 1914.

Full-size details of pilasters, etc.; signed E. G. 28. 10. 16.

Full-size details of top and bottom of tablet; signed E.G. Oct. 31 ' 16.

Rubbing of inscription; $36\frac{1}{2} \times 20\frac{1}{4}$; signed E.G. Feb. 1917.   [*See Plates X & XI*]

315 Tablet of Hopton-Wood stone with incised letters coloured in red and blue on north wall of Broxwood Roman Catholic Church, Leominster, Herefordshire, in memory of Lieut. RICHARD MARY SNEAD-COX, Royal Scots, killed in action 28th October, 1914, aged 21, and Lieut. GEOFFREY PHILIP JOSEPH SNEAD-COX, Royal Welch Fusiliers, killed in action 21st October, 1914, aged 19.

Rubbing; $35\frac{3}{4} \times 29\frac{1}{2}$; August 1915.

316 Cross of Portland stone in Wimbledon Cemetery in memory of HENRY CRAUFORD BARNARD, 1861–1915.

Pencil and wash drawing; signed E.G., Ditchling Common, Sx. 8 July 1915.

Full-size details; signed E.G. 16.12.15.

Pencil drawing for inscription; $12\frac{7}{8} \times 7\frac{3}{4}$; signed E.G. Dec. 20.15.

There are two pencil and wash drawings 1 in. scale; signed E.G. Ditchling Common, Sx., and dated respectively July 7 & 8 1915.

317 Hopton-Wood stone tablet commemorating the building in 1915 of hospital, by Ellen Odette Ulick O'Connor, wife of William, 4th Earl of Desart, in memory of OTWAY FREDERICK SEYMOUR CUFFE, 3rd son of Otway O'Connor, 3rd Earl of Desart.
Pencil drawing, full-size; $4\frac{3}{4} \times 4\frac{3}{4}$; signed Eric Gill, Ditchling Common, 11.2.16.

318 Headstone of Portland stone in churchyard of St. Mary the Virgin, Painswick, Glos., in memory of MARY CATHERINE GERE—1842–1916.
Pencil drawing (coloured); signed Eric Gill, Ditchling Common, Sx., 29.4.16 and another signed E.G. 19 May 1916.
There are also a sketch ($\frac{1}{8}$ f-s.) and full-size details both dated 19 July 1916.
Rubbing of inscription; $21\frac{1}{4} \times 10\frac{1}{4}$; signed E.G. Aug. 3, 1916.

319 Lettering on doors, etc., for the offices of the Crown Agents for the Colonies, Millbank, London.
In his diary for 1916 E.G. recorded several entries regarding lettering for this building under March 2 and 7 and on various dates to May 23.

320 Inscription on front of altar in the Chapel of the Incarnation, St. Osmund's, Parkstone, Dorset: CARO MEA VERE EST CIBUS SANGUIS MEUS VERE EST POTUS. Also lettering for cornice and door of Sacristy.
Inscription cut in 1916.

321 Brass plate in Winchester Cathedral in memory of PHILIP BERNARD WINGATE, Rector of Tarrant Keynston, 1904–1913, and of his Aunt.
Rubbing of inscription: $26\frac{1}{2} \times 15\frac{3}{4}$.
Engraved by Geo. T. Friend for E.G. September 1916.

322 Inscription of 550 $1\frac{1}{2}$ in. roman capitals on a panel of Grey Roman stone on a causeway between the island of St. Ermans and the mainland of Co. Donegal. It records the building of the causeway by the voluntary labour of the local people in memory of JOHN HAMILTON, J.P., D.L., of Brown-hall and St. Ermans, 1800–1884.
Full-size setting-out; $19\frac{1}{2} \times 68$; signed E.G. 12.9.16.

322A Tablet inscribed: AGNUS DEI QVI TOLLIS PECCATA MUNDI DONA NOBIS PACEM.
Rubbing; 8×18; endorsed 'cut by Albert Leaney [his first inscription] Sept. 1916 [letters slightly 'touched up' by E.G.]'.

323 Portland headstone in Willesden Cemetery in memory of ALPHONSE COURLANDER, d. October 1914.
Wash drawing; scale $1\frac{1}{2}$ in. = 1 ft.; signed Eric Gill, Ditchling Common, Sussex. 26.7.16.
Rubbing of inscription; $10\frac{1}{2} \times 16$; signed E.G. Oct. 30, 1916.

324 Recumbent gravestone of Forest of Dean stone near Stourbridge, Worcs., in memory of ALFRED LYTTELTON, 1857–1913.
E.G. made a sketch and three pencil drawings for suggested designs bearing dates in June–August 1915. The accepted design was made in October 1916. Actual size: $77 \times 28\frac{1}{2}$.
Work executed late 1916 and early 1917.

325 Hopton-Wood stone tablet (in a church near Malvern) in memory of EVERARD FERGUSON CALTHROP, 1876–1915.
Pencil drawing, $\frac{1}{6}$ f-s., with Coat of Arms in colour; signed E.G. Nov. 2 '16.
Rubbing dated November 1917; endorsed 'Drawn on the stone by E.G., cut by R. Beedham for E.G.'

326 Inscription on stone: DOMINE JESU CHRISTE QVI DIXISTI PETITE ET DABITUR VOBIS: DA MIHI GRATIAM UT ROGEM QUOD TIBI PLACEAT QVI VIVIS ET REGNAS DEUS PER OMNIA SAECULA SAECULORUM. AMEN.
Rubbing; $16\frac{3}{4} \times 21\frac{1}{4}$; endorsed by E.G. 'Cut by Albert Leaney, December 1916.'

327 Tablet of Hopton-Wood stone with incised letters, coloured in black and red, in . . . church, Glasgow, in memory of Captain ANDREW DONALD HUTTON.
Full-size drawing; $29\frac{3}{4} \times 23\frac{1}{4}$; signed Eric Gill Ditchling Common, Sx. 18 Dec. 1916.
Rubbing; $29\frac{1}{2} \times 21\frac{3}{4}$; cut by Albert Leaney, May 1917.

328 Memorial tablet of Hopton-Wood stone with incised letters, coloured black and red, in memory of Captain JOHN MACDONALD, Highland Light Infantry, killed in action at Gallipoli 13 July 1915.
Full-size drawing; $12\frac{3}{4} \times 23$; signed Eric Gill, Ditchling Common, Sx. 18 Dec. 1916.
Rubbing; $10\frac{3}{4} \times 20\frac{1}{2}$; cut by Albert Leaney, April 1917.
[In a church in or near Glasgow.]

329 Brass tablet inlaid in ebony panel with engraved letters coloured in black and red, in Royal Alexandra Hospital for Sick Children, Brighton, in memory of CHARLES CHETWODE BAILY, d. May 1914.
Full-size drawing; signed Eric Gill, Dec. 18. 1916; cut by George Friend.
Rubbing; $22\frac{1}{4} \times 21\frac{1}{4}$.

330 Tablet with a fourteen-line inscription of poem by Frances Cornford, *In Dorset*: FROM MUDDY ROAD TO MUDDY LANE I PLODDED THROUGH THE FALLING RAIN: . . .
Rubbing; 24×35; *c.* 1916.
[The poem first appeared in the collection of Frances Cornford's poems *Spring Morning* (Poetry Bookshop, 1915).]
[This inscription was probably cut by one of Eric Gill's pupils.]

331 Inscription in a church (whereabouts unknown):
BAD WORKMEN QUARREL WITH THEIR TOOLS
BECAUSE GOOD WORKMEN DO NOT USE BAD TOOLS
Rubbing; $11 \times 13\frac{1}{2}$; *c.* 1916.
[This inscription was probably cut by one of Eric Gill's pupils.]

331A Pen and ink drawing of alphabet for $1\frac{1}{2}$ in. wood letters in roman capitals.
The drawing of this alphabet is signed: 'Wood engraved alphabet. E.G. 1916 circa'.

332 Brass plate: THE CENTRAL LIBRARY FOR STUDENTS (London).
Full-size drawing; signed E.G. 13.1.17.
Rubbing: $9\frac{1}{2} \times 7\frac{1}{2}$.
[This Library was founded in 1916 by Dr. Albert Mansbridge, at 1 Galen Place, Bury Street, W.C.1. It was founded largely with a view to supplying books to the University Tutorial and Workers Education Association. The Library is now in the National Central Library, Malet Street, London, W.C.1.]

333 Tablet in white metal in memory of HUGH ARNOLD, Lieutenant, 8th Battn. Northumberland Fusiliers. Killed in action at Suvla Bay, August 1916, aged 43.
Full-size setting-out of lettering; 8×28; signed Eric Gill, Ditchling Common, Sx. 26.2.17.

E

334 Portland headstone, St. Andrew, Burgess Hill, Sussex, the inscription surmounted by a crucifix, in memory of JOHN EDWIN NYE, 1885–1916, who died of wounds received in the Great War.
Pencil drawing, $\frac{1}{8}$ full-size; signed Eric Gill, Ditchling Common, Sx., 26.2.17.

335 Wall tablet of Hopton-Wood stone in memory of IAN SAWERS SCOTT, 2nd Lieut., 2nd Battn. King's Own Scottish Borderers, killed in action 1 July 1916.
F-s. drawing; 12 × 19; signed Eric Gill, Ditchling Common, Sx.
Rubbing; 11$\frac{3}{4}$ × 19$\frac{1}{4}$; endorsed 'cut by Albert Leaney, June 1917.'

336 Inscription PASTOR EST TUI DOMINUS at foot of carving of the Holy face. This carving was built into the fabric above the entrance to Hopkins Crank where E.G. lived on Ditchling Common. After his departure in 1924 the carving was removed by his successor and ultimately sold to a collector in New York.
Rubbing of inscription; 3 × 14; signed E.G. 6.6.1917; endorsed 'at bottom of carving of the Holy Face made for D.P[epler].'

337 Wayside crucifix with pent roof at Bisham, Berks. In memory of FREDERIC SEPTIMUS KELLY and 14 other men of Bisham who gave their lives in the Great War 1914–1918.
Inscription on front panel of crucifix: JESU MY STRENGTH AND MY REDEEMER and on base: HERE WAS A ROYAL FELLOWSHIP OF DEATH.
Work executed August 1917.
(See also No. 344.)

338 Inscription in Latin incised direct on the South wall of the interior of the tower, St. Andrew's, Mells, Somerset (letters coloured in red and black) in memory of RAYMOND ASQUITH—1878–1916. This is surmounted by a bronze wreath designed by Sir Edwin Lutyens.
Work executed August 1917.
(See also No. 414.)

339 Hopton-Wood stone tablet on North wall of chancel in St. Mary's, Walberton, Arundel, in memory of PHILIP BLAKEWAY, Vicar of Walberton 1907–1915, Chaplain to the London Mounted Brigade who died on active service at Ismailia, June 16, 1915.
Tablet; 20 × 12.

Inscription laid out on stone by E.G. cut by Ralph J. Beedham, November 1917.

340 Portland stone tablet with an 8-line inscription in Latin and English: TU ES PETRUS ET SUPER . . . Lines 1, 2, 4, 6 and 8 are in Latin caps; lines 3, 5 and 7 in English lower-case.
Pen and ink drawing in red and black; unsigned and undated.
Actual size; 24 × 39. This was cut in March 1918.
[This was cut for exhibition purposes and was shown at the Alpine Club Gallery in May 1918. It is now to be seen built into a wall at Pigotts, North Dean, High Wycombe.]

340A Three-line inscription incised direct on the north wall in All Saints (the private chapel of the Manners family) Thorney Hill, Bransgore, Christchurch. The top line reads: JOHN MANNERS—1892–1914. The wording of the next two lines (written by Hon. John Fortescue) runs: TO THE BELOVED MEMORY OF A LIEUTENANT IN HIS MAJESTY'S FIRST OR GRENADIER REGIMENT OF FOOT GUARDS . . . KILLED IN ACTION SEPTEMBER 1 1914.
In front of the inscription is a bronze effigy of the deceased, the work of Bertram McKennal (1917).
Overall measurements of inscription 24 × 44. This was cut in April 1918.

341 Exhibition piece. Inscription IT LASTETH AND FOREVER SHALL FOR GOD LOVETH IT.
Rubbing of inscription; $5\frac{3}{4} \times 17\frac{1}{2}$; signed E.G. May 1918.

342 Stone carving of a pieta after a design by the Revd. Desmond Chute, bearing an inscription in Old French worded: MVLT AD APRIS KI BIEN CONUIST AHAN. ('He has learnt much who has known [much] suffering well.') From *The Song of Roland*, Line 2524, tirade 184.
Rubbing of pieta; $12\frac{3}{4} \times 17\frac{3}{4}$; signed 'Pieta. D.B.M.C[hute]. Oct. 1918 A.D.'

343 Hopton-Wood stone tablet, St. Eadburgha, Ebrington, Chipping Campden, Glos., in memory of EDWARD HORNBY, b. 1833, d. 1918. E.G., del.; J. Cribb, sc. July 1918.

344 Brass plate, with inscription in Latin, in Eton College Chapel in memory of FREDERIC SEPTIMUS KELLY, d. November 1916.
Full-size drawing; $14 \times 8\frac{1}{2}$; signed Eric Gill, Ditchling Common, Sx. 25.7.18.
Rubbing of inscription; $14 \times 8\frac{1}{2}$; July 1918.
(See also No. 337.)

345 Memorial in churchyard of St. Margaret's, Ditchling, in memory of WILLIAM WAKEFORD ATTREE, d. 1862, and of THOMAS ATTREE, d. 1863.
Rubbings of inscriptions; $9 \times 40\frac{1}{2}$ and $8\frac{1}{2} \times 47\frac{1}{2}$ respectively; August 1918.

346 Incised inscription in memory of Corporal WALTER HARVEY, d. September 1917.
Rubbing of portion of inscription; $4\frac{1}{2} \times 48\frac{3}{4}$; August 1918.

347 Village Cross of Purbeck Portland stone at Briantspuddle, Bere Regis, Dorset, in memory of those who gave their lives in the First World War. The cross is twenty-five feet high. On one side is the figure of Christ as the sufferer, beneath which are inscribed lines from the *Divine Revelations of Julian of Norwich*: IT IS SOOTH THAT SIN WAS CAUSE OF ALL THIS PAIN . . . On another side is a carving of Our Lady and the Christ Child. The work was carried out at intervals during 1916–1918 and was dedicated by the Bishop of Salisbury on September 12th, 1918.

348 Inscription on stone: OPTIMA ET PVLCHERRIMA VITAE SVPELLEX AMICITIA.
Rubbing; 4×27; signed E.G. August 1918.

349 Stone tablet, incised inscription, in memory of MARY ANNE WALLIS, d. April 1918.
Pen and ink sketch; signed E.G. 5.9.18.
Rubbing of inscription; $16\frac{1}{4} \times 25\frac{3}{4}$; signed Albert Leaney for E.G. Jan. 1919.

350 Inscription, in Greek, on holy water stoup commissioned by Frank Rinder: Π Η Γ Η · ΥΔΑΤΟΣ ('Christ the spring of water').
Rubbing; $3\frac{1}{2} \times 5\frac{3}{4}$; endorsed 'Drawn by E.G. cut by Albert Leaney, September 1918.'

351 Figure of Christ in Hopton-Wood stone, painted black, blue and red and with incised inscription: IESU, IESU, IESU ESTO MIHI IESUS.
Rubbing; $22\frac{1}{2} \times 26$; September 1918.
[Done in collaboration with Revd. D. B. M. Chute. Eric Gill's last carving prior to joining the Army, 12 September 1918.]

352 QUID SIBI VOLUNT ISTI?/ ET SI AD TE PERTINENT?/ RESPONDIT: PARVULI QUOS/ DONAVIT MIHI DEUS SERVO TUO.
Rubbing; $11\frac{1}{4} \times 37\frac{3}{4}$; *c.* 1918.

This is now in the S. Samuels collection, Liverpool. It seems unlikely, however, on stylistic evidence that the inscription is anything but the work of a pupil, and may be the piece (No. 128) submitted to the Alpine Club Gallery Exhibition, in London, May 1918. Be it noted, however, that in his diary under date of 26 July 1924, E.G. recorded: 'Re-cutting inscription "Quid sibi . . ." (for R. A. Walker) all day.'

353 Gravestone, with kerbing, of Portland stone in Brompton Cemetery, London, S.W., in memory of JANE, wife of ROBERT WHITEHEAD, d. August 1918 and of their son RONALD, d. November 1918.
Rubbing of inscription; 36½ × 11½; signed by Albert L. for E.G. March 1919.

354 Stone tablet in Rugby School Chapel, with portrait-bust, the work of Havard Thomas, in memory of Rupert Brooke. Incised beneath the bust: RUPERT BROOKE—1887–1915. This is followed by his poem *The Soldier* set out in full (the letters coloured).
Rubbing; 13¾ × 18¾; signed E. G., February 1919.

355 Recumbent gravestone in churchyard of St. Mary's Church, Storrington, Sussex, in memory of ARTHUR FRANCIS BELL. d. November 1918.
Pencil drawing; signed E.G. 18.3.19.

356 War Memorial Cross of Portland stone in the churchyard St. Mary, Harting, Sussex, in memory of those who gave their lives in the First World War.
Total height, above platform, about 22 feet. March 1919.
Quarter full-size details and ½ in. scale drawing; signed E.G. 20.5.20.

357 Gravestone with cross in the churchyard St. John the Baptist, Wivels-field, Sussex, in memory of RICHARD TYRELL GODMAN,—1911–1918.
Full-size details for cross; signed E.G. 21.3.19.

358 Hopton-Wood stone tablet in the cloisters of the Priory of Our Lady of Good Counsel, Haywards Heath, Sussex. The inscription, in Latin, records the granting of an indulgence by the Bishop of Southwark.
Size of tablet: 14½ × 14½.
Pencil drawing; signed E.G. 27.3.19.
Work executed March 1919.

359 Memorial of Portland stone at Chirk, near Wrexham, in memory of those who gave their lives in the First World War. This stands about 15 feet high.

On the south face is a bas-relief of a soldier 'on watch' with right hand holding rifle and left hand upraised: tin-hatted and great-coated. Inscriptions of seventy names in English and Welsh on all four sides of the base.

The work was conceived in March 1919 and carried out at intervals during 1920.

'Soldier on the look out—the most typical attitude representing the war of entrenchment.' quoted from a note from E.G. to Lord Howard de Walden who commissioned the memorial.

360 Tombstone in Wivelsfield Churchyard, Haywards Heath, in memory of ANNIE TRUMBLE, d. September 1917.
Pencil and wash drawing of cross; signed E.G. 9.4.19.
Rubbing of inscription; $12 \times 8\frac{1}{4}$; signed Albert L[eaney] for E.G., June 1919.

361 War Memorial tablet of Hopton-Wood stone, St. Mary the Virgin, Cloughton, Yorks., in memory of those who gave their lives in the Great War, 1914–18.
The Memorial ($40\frac{3}{4} \times 48$) comprises some 298 letters, coloured and incised and four raised letters, gilded, with a laurel leaf in relief.
Pencil drawing (lettered in red and black); signed E.G. 18.4.19.
Rubbing of portion of inscription; signed H.J.C., Oct. 1919.

362 Headstone in Portland stone, surmounted by crucifix, in Godalming Cemetery, Surrey, in memory of CARL TRESSLER, 1851–1918.
Drawing ($\frac{1}{8}$ full-size) of detail of headstone and full-size details of top and portion of inscription; $9\frac{1}{2} \times 5$; signed E.G. 17.6.19.

363 War memorial pillar erected by public subscription at Ditchling, Sussex, for the men of Ditchling who lost their lives in the First World War.
The names of twenty men are incised on the South face of this pillar. The words *Greater love hath no man than this, that he lay down his life for his friends.* are incised in $2\frac{1}{2}$ in. letters around the plinth of the memorial.
Pencil drawing (tinted); $10\frac{1}{2} \times 7\frac{1}{2}$; endorsed 'Proposed Ditchling War Monument' and signed E.G. 6.7.1919.

364 Hopton-Wood stone tablet, St. George the Martyr, Ham, Kent, in memory of those who lost their lives in the Great War 1914–1918.
Size of tablet: $24\frac{3}{4} \times 42$. There are 273 $1\frac{1}{8}$ in. letters incised and coloured.
Pencil sketch; signed E.G. 15.8.19.
Work carried out by J. Cribb and G. Tomsett Oct.–Nov. 1919.

365 War Memorial tablet of light Hopton-Wood stone in Main Entrance
Hall of the Victoria and Albert Museum, Cromwell Road, South Kensington,
commemorating members of the staff of the Museum who fell in the Great
War, 1914–1918. There are 252 incised letters, painted.
Pencil drawing; 1 in. scale; signed E.G. 19.9.19.
Rubbing; signed H.J.C.
Actual size of tablet; 58 × 26.
Work executed February 1920.
Unlike the vast majority of E.G.'s inscriptional work this tablet is 'signed'.
On the bottom left corner the initials: J C; and on the bottom right: E G.
These initials are carved on either side of the letters V & A in monogram, thus:
J♅C E♅G.

366 Headstone of Hopton-Wood stone in Roman Catholic Cemetery, Kensal
Green, in memory of VIOLET MARY HOLLAND—1881–1918.
Pencil drawing; (tinted) 1 in. scale; signed E.G. 19.9.19.
Actual size of headstone: 40½ × 22.

367 Inscription on base of cross in the churchyard SS. Peter & Paul, Hareby,
Spilsby, Lincs., in memory of MARIAN HAIRBY WINGATE, born
November 3, 1826, died March 18, 1916.
Pen and ink sketch; signed E.G. 25.6.19.
Rubbing; 10½ × 15½; signed H.J.C. for E.G., Oct. 1919.

368 Headstone in memory of WILLIAM HERBERT BOND 1862–1918,
Headmaster of Brighton Municipal School of Art, 1905–1918.
Pen and ink sketch; signed E.G. 1.7.19.
Rubbing of inscription; 15 × 11; signed Albert L. for E.G. Nov. 1919.

369 Tablet in memory of GERRARD CHOWNE, Artist, 1875–1917.
Pencil sketch; signed E.G. 26.5.19. and endorsed 'Tonks Tablet'.
Rubbing; 20¼ × 25¼; signed Albert L. for E.G. November 1919.

370 Stone tablet beneath a statue of St. George on North wall in the Clere
Chapel, St. Mary the Virgin, Rye, Sussex, in memory of Vice-Admiral
Sir GEORGE WARRENDER, Bt., K.C.B., d. 1917.
Size of tablet; 6½ × 9.
Rubbing; signed A.L. for E.G. DEC. 1919.

371 Oak panel for house occupied by Francis and Frances Cornford, in
Cambridge: CONDUIT HEAD MADINGLEY ROAD. This direction

board (which was destroyed by vandals) bore twenty-three letters $2\frac{3}{4}$ in. and five of 1 in. incised and painted, was carved in January 1920.
(See also No. 210.)

372 Portland stone tablet in Winchester Cathedral, inscription surmounted by Coat of Arms, in memory of Brigadier-General JOHN EDMOND GOUGH, V.C., C.B., C.M.G. b. 1871, died of wounds February 1915.
First drawing $\frac{1}{8}$th full-size; signed E.G. 24.5.18. A second drawing (coloured) 1 in. scale is signed E.G. 7.1.20.
A third drawing (coloured) (the accepted design); 1 in. scale; signed E.G. Ditchling Common, Sx. 3.1.21.
There is also a full-size drawing of the Coat of Arms and part of inscription (in colour); 32×22; signed E.G. 4.1.21.
Rubbing of inscription; $41 \times 28\frac{1}{4}$; January 1920.   [*See Plate X*]

373 Inscribed tablet, with portrait head in St. Michael's, Amberley, Sussex, in memory of JOAN MARY STRATTON, d. April 1919 aged 17 years.
Rubbing of inscription; $24 \times 11\frac{1}{2}$; signed Albert L[eaney] inscrip., E.G. head, Jan. 1920.

374 War Memorial tablet of Hopton-Wood stone in St. Mary's, Betteshanger, Kent, in memory of those who fell in the Great War 1914–1918.
Full-size drawing; $30 \times 24\frac{1}{4}$; signed Eric Gill, 1.3.20.
Rubbing; signed George Tomsett for E.G. Ap. 1920.

375 Memorial tablet of Hopton-Wood stone formerly in St. Luke's Church, West Holloway, London, N.7, in memory of RICHARD GLOVER, D.D., 1837–1919. Dr. Glover was the first Vicar of this parish (1869–1898).
Drawing; 1 in. scale; signed E.G. 18.3.20.
[This tablet was destroyed when the church was badly damaged by enemy action during World War II.]

376 Inscription on plinth of equestrian statue on the Horse Guards Parade, London, in memory of GARNET JOSEPH WOLSELEY, Viscount Wolseley, 1833–1913.
Cut by H. J. Cribb, April 1920.

377 Memorial tablet of Portland stone, letters incised and coloured, in St. Peter & St. Paul, West Wittering, Chichester, for the men of the parish who fell in the Great War, 1914–1918.

Pencil drawing (tinted); scale 1 in.; signed E.G. 19.4.20.
Full-size detail of corner, showing portion of inscription in red and black; signed E.G. 20.4.20.
Rubbing; $28\frac{1}{2} \times 32\frac{3}{4}$.
[E.G.'s father, the Revd. A. T. Gill, was at this date Vicar of the Parish.]

378 Inscriptions on sides of a garden roller 18 in. diameter: COME ALL YOU FALSE YOUNG MEN DO NOT LEAVE ME HERE TO COMPLAIN and FOR THE GRASS THAT HAS OFTEN TIMES BEEN TRAMPLED UNDER FOOT GIVE IT TIME IT WILL RISE UP AGAIN.
Rubbings; endorsed by E.G. 'Albert Leaney for E.G. April 1920.'
[This garden roller was thus inscribed for the late Mrs. Ethel Mairet of Gospels, Ditchling, Sussex, and is now in the possession of Mr. and Mrs. A. E. Southern at the same address.]

379 Hopton-Wood stone tablet for Melbourne Museum, Australia, recording a gift by JOHN CONNELL in February 1914. (The tablet was commissioned by Mrs. Frank Rinder, Cambridge.)
Size of tablet: $12 \times 14\frac{3}{4}$; rubbing, endorsed by E.G, 'H.J.C. for E.G. November, 1920.'

379A Inscription: OPERA MANUUM NOSTRARUM DIRIGE SUPER NOS ET OPUS MANUUM NOSTRARUM DIRIGE.
Rubbing; $12\frac{1}{4} \times 18$; endorsed 'By Hilary Stratton, June 1920.'

379B Inscriptions; Latin and English in alternate lines, the Latin in roman capitals (black), the English lower-case (red).
They read: HOMINES DIVITES IN VIRTUTE . . . and 'Men rich in virtue studying beautifulness'.
Water-colour drawing; $13\frac{3}{4} \times 29$; endorsed 'Drawn by Hilary Stratton, (E.G. helping) June 1920'.

380 Village Cross at Angmering, Sussex, with inscription on base in remembrance of those who served and died in the Great War 1914–1918.
Quarter f-s. detail of lettering; signed Eric Gill, Ditchling Common, Sx., 1.7.20.

381 Memorial in chancel St. Peter's, Stanway, Glos., and another for a window in the same church. Both commemorate the eleven men of Stanway

who gave their lives in the Great War, 1914–1918. The inscription in the chancel reads:

MEN OF STANWAY / 1914–1918 / FOR A TOMB / THEY HAVE AN ALTAR / FOR LAMENTATION / MEMORY / AND FOR PITY / PRAISE, and: FOR YOUR TO-MORROW WE GAVE OUR TO-DAY.

The inscription for the window records, in two panels, the names of the men commemorated.

Layout for chancel inscriptions signed E.G. 1.9.20.

Inscription for window; 1 in. scale; signed E.G. 17.8.20.

[These memorials were commissioned by the Countess of Wemyss.]

382 Memorial Cross and Gravestone in the crypt of St. Paul's Cathedral, London, in memory of Field-Marshal Earl FREDERICK SLEIGH ROBERTS, V.C., 1832–1914.

The cross, of black polished Hopton-Wood stone, is on the wall; the single name ROBERTS incised on base and coloured. This is flanked by regimental colours. The gravestone, a slab of York stone, is at the foot of the cross, inscribed: ROBERTS / INDIA / 1832 / FRANCE / 1914.

Pencil drawing (coloured); 1 in. scale; signed E.G. 3.11.20. and an alternative design, in pen and ink, signed E.G. 4.6.21.   [*See Plate XI*]

383 Bronze tablet in Eton College Chapel, the inscription surmounted by Coat of Arms, in memory of Major Lord DESMOND FITZGERALD, M.C. 1888–1916 1st Battn., Irish Guards, 2nd Son of 5th Duke of Leinster and of HERMIONE his wife.

Pencil drawing; ¼ full-size; signed E.G. 3.11.20.

384 Headstone of Portland in memory of MONICA SHOVE, 1883–1919. Two pencil sketches; signed E.G. 5.11.20.

385 Inscription in memory of ELIZABETH SILVESTER of the Slade School, Gower Street, London, d. March 1920 aged 80 years.

Rubbing of inscription (undated); $6\frac{3}{4} \times 42\frac{1}{4}$.

Work executed *c.* 1920.

386 The fourteen Stations of the Cross carved in low relief (originally painted in tempera) on Beer stone, in St. Cuthbert's (R.C.) Church, Bradford.

Texts incised in either Greek or Latin; titles in English.

Actual size of each Station; 30 × 30; 1921–24.
[The designs of the majority of these Stations were after drawings made by the Revd. Desmond Chute.]

387 Circular tablet of Portland stone in Winchester Cathedral, in memory of Brigadier-General RONALD CAMPBELL MACLACHAN, D.S.O., 1872–1917.
Pencil drawing; 1 in. scale; signed E.G. 4.1.21.
Full-size drawing; 23½ in. in diameter; signed E.G. 5.1.21.

388 Headstone of Portland stone, with inscription in Latin, in memory of LENAE UNICAE BRYANI MILMAN, 1862–1914.
Pencil drawing (in wash); signed Eric Gill, Ditchling Common, Sx. 12.1.21.

389 Tablet of Portland stone incised letters in red and blue, surmounted by a Coat of Arms, over the doorway leading to the gallery, All Saints, Thorneyhill, Bransgore, Christchurch, Hants. The inscription runs: THIS STONE IS SET HERE IN TOKEN OF OUR LOVE AND GRATITUDE. FOUR HUNDRED OFFICERS OF THE NEW ZEALAND EXPE-DITIONARY FORCE.
They were nursed at Avon Tyrell near-by, during the war 1914–1918.
Pencil drawing; signed Eric Gill 12 January 1921.
Size of tablet: 34 × 14.
Executed January–February 1922.

389A Exhibition piece: MATER AMABILIS ORA PRO NOBIS.
Rubbing; 1¾ × 42; signed A. Leaney for Eric Gill. 25.2.1921.

390 Marble tablet, with inscription in French, in Cambrai Cathedral, in memory of EDWARD WILLIAM HORNER 1888–1917 of Mells, Somerset. Lieut. 18th Hussars, killed in action 21 November 1917.
Pencil sketch; signed E.G. 12.1.21.
Rubbing; 23½ × 15¾; signed E.G. Feb. 1921.

391 Tablet on the outside wall near West door of All Saints' Church, St. John's Wood, N.W.8, in memory of HARRY COULTER, b. 3 June, 1887, d. 19 October, 1920.
Size of tablet: 12 × 24.
Work executed 1921.

392 Hopton-Wood stone tablet in All Saints' Church, Debach, Woodbridge, Suffolk, in memory of MARIAN ALLBUTT, b. 24 Dec. 1840, d. 18 May, 1910.

Rubbing of inscription; $14\frac{3}{4} \times 28$; signed H.J.C. for E.G., Feb 1921.

393 Gravestone of Hopton-Wood stone in memory of ROSALIND MARY NASH, 1904–1920.

Pencil drawing, $\frac{1}{8}$f-s.; signed E.G. 22.3.21.

Rubbing of inscription; $6\frac{1}{2} \times 23\frac{3}{4}$; signed A.L. May 21 '21.

394 Incised lettering on a pilaster of the British Museum—the War Memorial for the men from this museum who fell in the Great War 1914–1918.

Full-size detail of letters; signed E.G. 2.5.21.

(See also No. 220.)

395 Inscription, in Latin, on wall by steps leading to the Lady Chapel, Downside Abbey, Bath, in memory of EDMUND BISHOP, d. 19 February 1917.

Sketch of memorial; 1 in. scale; signed E.G. 4.5.21.

Full-size drawing, of portion of inscription, unsigned and undated.

396 War Memorial Cross at Trumpington, Cambs., in memory of those who fell in the Great War 1914–1918. A considerable job with the names inscribed on panels.

Various sketches submitted to the Memorial Committee were dated May & June 1921.

Sketch in red and black; $\frac{1}{2}$ in. scale; endorsed: 'Wide revised setting out. No. 5'; signed E.G. 23.5.21. and another, similar to the above, signed E.G. 22.6.21.

397 Monument at Dunmow, Essex, in memory of the men who fell in the First World War, 1914–1918.

Full-size drawing of names; $8 \times 26\frac{1}{2}$; signed E.G. 24.5.21.

398 War Memorial of Hopton-Wood stone in ante-chapel New College, Oxford, commemorating members of the College who gave their lives in the Great War 1914–1919. Some 228 names are recorded which together with the inscription at the top, comprise some 5,085 letters and figures.

Rubbing of portion of inscription; $16\frac{1}{2} \times 52\frac{1}{2}$; June–September 1921.

[In this work E.G.'s assistants were H. J. Laurie Cribb for letter-cutting and David Jones for letter-painting.]

399 Tablet of Portland stone fixed on corbels in the Slade School of Fine Arts, Gower Street, London, in memory of students who lost their lives in the Great War 1914–1918.
Rubbing; 34 × 24; August 1921.

400 Cruciform gravestone at All Saints, Bisham, Marlow, Bucks., in memory of JOHN HARRY SEPTIMUS KELLY, Born June 18, 1917 died August 1, 1921.
Pencil drawing of gravestone and cross signed Eric Gill, 11.11.21.
Rubbing of emblems and Greek letters endorsed 'Cut by D.B.M.C[hute] on temporary cross for Mrs. Kelly, August A.D. 1918.'

401 War memorial panel on slab of Euville stone at S. Dominic's Priory, Southampton Road, London, N.W.5, commemorating those who fell in the Great War, 1914–1919.
Actual size of panel; $52\frac{3}{4} \times 72\frac{3}{4}$.
Sketch $\frac{1}{8}$f-s. in red and black; signed E.G. 21.10.21.
The inscription runs: A.D. 1914–1918. A STONE OF REMEM-BRANCE FROM THE SOIL OF FRANCE. PRAY FOR MEN OF THIS PARISH WHO DIED IN THE WAR. Here follow the names in thirteen lines of incised $1\frac{3}{4}$ in. caps, in red and blue, below which are two lines of Laurence Binyon's poem. 'They shall grow not old . . .'

401A Headstone in memory of ALFRED WRIGHT STEELE, d. March 1910 and of EDNA, his wife, d. December 1912. Also of their daughter EMILY ELIZABETH STEELE, d. March 1921.
Rubbing; 20 × 30.
Work executed by E.G. and Joseph Cribb, c. 1921.

401B Inscription: O YE FIRE AND HEAT BLESS THE LORD PRAISE HIM AND MAGNIFY HIM FOR EVER
Rubbing; $9\frac{1}{2} \times 17\frac{1}{2}$; signed Albert L. for E.G. Oct. 1921.

402 War Memorial tablet of Hopton-Wood stone, St. Agatha's, Coates, Fittleworth, Sussex, in memory of men of the Parish who fell in the Great War, 1914–1918.
Size of tablet; 24 × 19; drawing, $\frac{1}{8}$ full-size; signed E.G. 2.1.22.

403 Headstone of Green Hornton stone in memory of HERVEY FISHER, 1873–1921.
Pen and ink sketch; signed E.G. 16.2.22. Ditchling Common, Sx.

404 War Memorial tablet of Hopton-Wood stone commemorating employees of W. H. & F. J. Horniman & Company, Ltd., who fell in the Great War, 1914–1918. This is in the vestibule of the firm's Head Office, Shepherdess Walk, London, N.1.

Sketch; $\frac{1}{8}$ f-s.; signed E.G. 17.2.22.

Rubbing; $39\frac{1}{2} \times 18$; signed H. J. Cribb for Eric Gill. July 1922.

405 Gravestone of Hopton-Wood stone, surmounted by a crucifix, in Kensal Green Cemetery, London, in memory of MARIGOLD, daughter of Winston and Clementine Churchill, 1918–1921.

Pencil drawing; $1\frac{1}{4}$ in. scale; signed E.G. 1.4.22.

406 Memorial tablet of Hopton-Wood stone in the Royal College of Music, Prince Consort Road, London, S.W.7, commemorating those who fell in the Great War 1914–1918.

Drawing, in red and black ink; signed E.G. 5.4.22.

Rubbing of portion of inscription; $24\frac{3}{4} \times 22\frac{1}{2}$; signed H. J. Cribb for Eric Gill Oct. 1922.

407 Inscription on Memorial gateway of Bath stone, Clifton College, Bristol to the memory of 3063 Cliftonians who served and 578 who fell in the Great War 1914–1919.

[The inscription comprises 550 names of 7,200 letters, i.e. 3,600 letters on each side of gateway cut direct on the wall.]

Pencil drawing; 1 in. scale; signed E.G. 25.4.22.

408 Hopton-Wood stone plaque in the Memorial Hall, Worplesdon, Surrey, commemorating the building of the Hall in 1921 in honour of the men of Worplesdon who served and in memory of those who fell in the Great War, 1914–18.

Rubbing; $17\frac{1}{2} \times 23\frac{1}{4}$; signed H. J. Cribb for Eric Gill, 30 June 1922.

409 Headstone of Portland stone, St. Martin, Westmeston, Sussex, in memory of PETER NEWNHAM, d. November 1916, aged 71 years.

Pencil drawing; 1 in. scale; signed Eric Gill, Ditchling Common, Sx. 1.7.22.

410 Mural tablet of Hopton-Wood stone in St. Agatha's, Gilling, Richmond, Yorks., in memory of THOMAS PERCY PEMBERTON, 1833–1921, M.A., J.P., Vicar of the Parish 1870–1901.

Drawing, in red and black ink; $\frac{1}{8}$ f-s.; signed E.G. 24.7.22.

Actual size of tablet; approx 42×33.

411 Mural tablet, with inscription in Latin, St. Margaret, Ditchling, in memory of OLOF ALICE JOHNSTON, d. 11 February, 1917. [A sister of Edward Johnston.]
Work executed c. 1922.

412 Inscriptions on slate for a sundial for Lord Carmichael; GLORIA IN ALTISSIMIS DEO and IN TERRA PAX . . .
Rubbings of inscriptions; $9\frac{3}{4} \times 20\frac{3}{4}$ and $5\frac{3}{4} \times 32\frac{1}{2}$; endorsed '(Slate) E.G. for Lord Carmichael. Dec. 29.3.22.'

413 Inscription cut on Portland stone: HOMINES DIVITES IN VIRTUTE / PULCHRITUDINIS STUDIUM HABENTES / . . .
Pen and ink sketch; signed E.G. 2.8.22.
Rubbing; 9×35; endorsed 'Drawn and cut by E.G. Aug. '22'.
[This work was commissioned by Lord Carmichael.]

414 Tablet on South wall of Amiens Cathedral, the inscription in French and Latin, in memory of RAYMOND ASQUITH, 1878–1916, Lieutenant, Grenadier Guards, killed in action at Guinchy, 15 September 1916. The inscription was phrased by Katherine Asquith assisted by Hilaire Belloc.
Tablet; $25\frac{1}{2} \times 17\frac{3}{4}$.
Work executed September 1922.
(Cf. No. 338.)   [See Plate XII]

415 Sundial of Portland stone at Ditchling, Sussex, with inscription in memory of ANTHONY WALLIS, 1879–1919.
Height; 39 in. (approx.).
Drawings; signed E.G. 29.11.22.

416 Slate tablet set on a Portland stone frame surmounted by Coat of Arms, on S. Wall St. Dunstan, Mayfield, Sussex, in memory of APSLEY PHILIP TREHERNE, 1872–1922 also of GEORGINA WELDON, 1837–1914, daughter of Morgan Treherne of Gate House, Mayfield.
Size of tablet; 36×26.
Pen and ink sketch; undated and unsigned but made, according to E.G.'s diary, 30 November 1922.

417 Incised inscription on small oak tablet in memory of . . . DRAPER.
Cut by Laurie Cribb in 1922.

418 War Memorial of Portland stone (6 ft. $\times$ 16 ft.) on the wall of the Library, Leeds University, depicting Christ driving the moneychangers out of the

Temple. Along the cornice is inscribed, in Latin, a passage adapted from the Vulgate version of St. James's Epistle, v., 1: AGITE NUNC DIVITES PLORATE ULULANTES IN MISERIIS VESTRIS . . . The right-hand panel carries a 9-line inscription, also in Latin, from St. John's Gospel, ii., 15: ET CUM FECISSET QUASI FLAGELLUM DE FUNICULIS . . . The work was executed 1922–23 and unveiled by the Bishop of Ripon, June 1, 1923.

419 Mural tablet of Hopton-Wood stone in the cloister New College, Oxford, in memory of HENRY ERLE RICHARDS, K.C.S.I., K.C., M.A., B.C.L., 1861–1922.
Actual size: 18¾ × 29.
Drawing; signed E.G. 29.1.23.

420 Raised ledger stone of Portland stone, St. Michael, Wilsford, nr. Amesbury, Wilts., in memory of WYNLANE, wife of Oliver William Foster Lodge, d. September 1922.
Pen and ink drawing; signed E.G. 29.1.23.
On the reverse of this stone Oliver William Foster Lodge, 1878–1955, is commemorated, but this inscription was carved by Sydney Sheppard, 1956. Beneath it, however, is an inscription 'JOURNEYS END IN LOVERS MEETING' which was cut earlier by E.G.
(See also No. 421.)

421 Slate tablet, figures in low relief, on north wall, St. Michael Wilsford, nr. Amesbury, Wilts., in memory of WYNLANE, wife of Oliver William Foster LODGE of Upper Holcombe, Painswick, d. September 2nd, 1922.
Pencil drawing; ⅛ f-s.; signed E.G. 6.2.23.
Rubbing of tablet; 31 × 12¾; signed E.G. March 1923.
(See also No. 420.)

422 Alabaster tablet in Chichester Cathedral in memory of HENRY HOLDING MOORE, 1839–1911, for 44 years sacristan of the Cathedral.
Sketch; ¼ full-size; signed E.G. 4.9.22.
Rubbing; 10 × 19; signed E.G. Mar. 1923.
[H. H. Moore was Eric Gill's father-in-law.]
(See also No. 568.)

423 Headstone of Chambon stone with Hopton-Wood stone panel inserted, in memory of AGNES ELIZABETH MURRAY, 1894–1922, daughter of

Prof. Gilbert and Lady Mary Murray, buried near Clermont-Ferrand, Puy-de-Dôme, France.
Pencil drawing; signed E.G. 29.1.23.
Rubbing of inscription; $12\frac{1}{4} \times 20\frac{1}{2}$; signed A.L. sc. for E.G. March 1923.

424 Cross in Portland stone at Logie Coldstone, Dinnet, Aberdeenshire, in memory of JOHN CHRISTOPHER CARTER, d. January 1923.
Pencil drawing (tinted); 1 in. scale; signed E.G. 9.3.23.

425 Three headstones, adjacent to each other, St. Mary, Gilston, nr. Harlow. They are of Hopton-Wood stone and (L. to R.) in memory of: REGINALD EDEN JOHNSTON, 1847–1922, shows a carving in low relief of the B.V.M.; GEOFFREY STEWART JOHNSTON, 1889–1915, a cross; ROSE ALICE JOHNSTON, 1854–1907, shows a carving in low relief of St. John the Evangelist.
Pencil sketch and drawing; signed E.G. 10.3.23.

426 Hopton-Wood stone tablet at East Carlton, Market Harborough, Leicester, in memory of the Rt. Hon. NATHANIEL, BARON LINDLEY, P.C., F.R.S., 1828–1921.
Rubbing of inscription; $31 \times 23\frac{3}{4}$; signed H. J. Cribb for Eric Gill, May 1923.

427 Marble tablet in the Cloisters, Westminster Abbey, in memory of WALTER HINES PAGE, 1885–1918. Ambassador of the United States of America to the Court of St. James, 1913–1918.
Rough sketch; unsigned and undated. Sketch in red and black, numbered '2'; signed E.G. June 1923.
Rough layout of full-size letters; signed E.G. 8.6.23.
Pencil drawing; $\frac{1}{4}$ f-s.; signed Eric Gill, Ditchling Common, Sx. 21.4.23.
Rubbing of inscription; $23 \times 17\frac{1}{4}$; signed E.G. June 1923. [See Plate XIII]

428 Headstone in Portland stone with inscription surmounted by a carving of the Holy Child, in memory of MARY CUMING, born June 7, 1912, died July 1, 1921.
Pencil drawing; $1\frac{1}{4}$ scale; signed E.G. 5.6.23.

429 Portland headstone for grave of SIEGMUND ALFRED SCHNAPPER, 1864–1922.
Pencil drawing (coloured); $1\frac{1}{4}$ in. scale; signed E.G. 5.6.23.

430 Brass tablet in Stowe School, Bucks., to commemorate the occasion on June 26th 1923, when Sir Owen Seaman, on behalf of the Trustees of the Agenda Club, placed the Agenda Samurai Sword in the keeping of the School. Drawing in red and black, $\frac{1}{4}$ full-size, numbered ' 1 '. Another, similar to above, numbered ' 2 '. Both signed E.G. 5.6.23.
Rubbing; $10\frac{3}{4} \times 13\frac{3}{4}$; signed A.L. for E.G. June 1923.

431 Foundation Stone of the Royal Northern Hospital, Holloway Road, London, laid by the Lady Patricia Ramsay, 12 July 1923.
Pencil sketch for inscription; 1 in. scale; signed E.G. 2.7.23.

432 Gravestone in Kensal Green Cemetery, London, in memory of ALICE MEYNELL, d. 1922.
Pencil drawing; 1 in. scale; signed E.G. 23.7.23 revised 17.8.23.

433 Tablet with incised inscription, in the Chapel of the Guards' depot, Caterham, Surrey, commemorating the gift of Colours carried by the 1st Battn. Coldstream Guards, 1857–1872 and presented in memory of Major-General Sir GEOFFREY FEILDING, K.C.B., C.M.G., D.S.O.
Full-size sketch with inscription in full; signed E.G. 25.4.23.
Rubbing of tablet for Colours of 1st Batt. Coldstream Guards; $15\frac{1}{4} \times 20\frac{1}{4}$; signed H.J.C. for E.G. Aug. '23.

434 Monument of Portland stone at Broad Chalke, Salisbury, in memory of MAURICE HEWLETT, Poet, 1861–1923.
Pencil drawing of front and back of pillar; $\frac{1}{8}$ full-size; signed E.G. 6.7.23.
Rubbing of inscription; $21\frac{3}{4} \times 14\frac{1}{2}$; signed E.G. del., H.J.C. sc. Oct. '23.

435 Hopton-Wood gravestone with kerbing at Northwood, Middlesex, in memory of CONSTANCE EVELYN TYSER, 1884–1922.
Three pencil drawings all $\frac{1}{12}$ full-size; (a) signed E.G. 6.2.23. (b) signed E.G. 14.2.23. and (c) signed Eric Gill, Ditchling Common, 22.5.23.
Rubbing of inscription; $15 \times 10\frac{1}{2}$; signed E.G. Oct. 22–4, '23.

436 Foundation stone for the chapel of the Russell School, Ballard's, Addington, nr. Croydon.
Rubbing of portion of inscription: SEQVIMVR in 10 in. letters; $10 \times 90\frac{1}{2}$; signed E.G. 5.10.23.
There is also the architect's (Aston Webb & Son) drawing for the chapel, dated 27 March 1925. There were also several other inscriptions in various

parts of the school cut in 1925. This was the Royal Warehousemen, Clerks & Drapers' School. Its title has recently been changed to the Royal Russell School.

437 War Memorial in memory of the men of the Borough of Islington who gave their lives in the Great War, 1914–1918. This is over the entrance to the Casualty Department of the Royal Northern Hospital, Holloway Road, London, N.
Rubbing of inscription; $34 \times 29\frac{1}{2}$; signed H.J.C. for E.G. Nov. 1923.

438 Gravestone in Boulogne in memory of HERBERT TRENCH, 1865–1923.
Rubbing of inscription; $6 \times 25\frac{1}{4}$; signed E.G. December 1923.

439 Inscription; O WANELESS ONE THAT ART THE CORE / OF EVERY HEART'S UNKNOWN DESIRE / TAKE BACK THE HEARTS THAT BEAT NO MORE.
Rubbing of inscription; 6×35; signed E.G. December 1923.

440 Memorial tablet of zinc in the Children's Hospital, Brighton, recording the gift of money to the hospital in 1922 in memory of ANNE HALL.
Pen and ink drawings, $\frac{1}{8}$ full-size; in E.G.'s hand but neither signed nor dated.
Rubbing of tablet; $18 \times 14\frac{1}{2}$.
Work executed c. 1923.

441 Memorial tablet of Portland stone, surmounted by Coat of Arms, in Sir Roger Manwood's School, Sandwich, Kent, in memory of those who fell in the Great War 1914–1918.
Drawing; $\frac{1}{12}$ full-size; signed E.G. 4.1.24.

442 Inscription on a sundial: PENSA CHE QUESTA DI MAI NON RAGGIORNA.
Rubbing of inscription; $17\frac{3}{4} \times 14\frac{1}{2}$; January 1924.
The border and dial lines were cut by Philip Hagreen.
[N.B. The words QUESTA DI are perhaps in error for QUESTO DÌ.]

443 Small silver plate for library table in the Overseas Club, St. James' Street, London, recording the gift of the table in memory of the Hon. CHARLES THOMAS MILLS, Lieut., Scots Guards, killed in action October 1915.
Pen and ink sketch; signed E.G. 21 March, 1924.
Rubbing of plate; $7 \times 4\frac{1}{2}$.

444 Portland headstone in Brookwood Cemetery, Woking, in memory of ERNEST SYRETT, d. February 1906 and of MARIAN SYRETT, d. September 1923.
Pen and ink sketch; signed E.G. 1.6.24.
Rubbing of inscription; $11\frac{3}{4} \times 10\frac{1}{2}$; endorsed 'Cut by Laurie Cribb, (E.G. del.) June 1924'.

445 Gravestone of Portland, surmounted by a cross in memory of LOUISE SHAW, 1867–1923.
Pencil and wash drawing; 1 in. scale; signed E.G. 21.6.24.
Actual height: 51 in.

446 Portland headstone in churchyard of St. Mary, Storrington, Sussex, in memory of PEGGY SUTTON, 1885–1923.
Two pencil drawings both $1\frac{1}{8}$ full-size; signed E.G. 1.12.23.
Rubbing of inscription; $14 \times 13\frac{1}{2}$; signed Laurie Cribb sc., E.G. del. June 1924.

447 Wall tablet of Hopton-Wood stone, in Brighton, inscription surmounted by a carving of dolphins, for site of Russell House, Brighton, occupied by RICHARD RUSSELL, M.D., F.R.S. from 1754 until his death in 1759.
Full-size drawing; $23\frac{1}{2} \times 18$; signed E.G. 24.6.24.
Rubbing of tablet; signed L.C. for E.G. March 1933.
This was the first of several similar tablets commissioned by the Corporation of Brighton. Others were: Nos. 458, 459, 493, 494, 502, 525 and 551.

448 Sculptured profile portrait and inscription in the foyer of St. Martin's Theatre, Shaftesbury Avenue, London; lettered: REMEMBER MEGGIE ALBANESI AN ARTIST WHO DIED IN THE SERVICE OF THE THEATRE DECEMBER 9 1923 R.I.P.
Rubbing; $28\frac{1}{2} \times 14$; signed E.G. June 1924.

449 Funeral urn, with inscription on base, in Willesden Cemetery, in memory of WALTER MORTIMER RONALDS, 1902–1924.
Drawings signed E.G. 26.6.24. and 8.5.25.
Rubbing; $6\frac{1}{4} \times 6\frac{3}{4}$; signed E.G. del., L.C. sc. June '26.

450 Headstone of Hopton-Wood stone, surmounted by a cross, in memory of WILLIAM MOODIE, d. June 1923 aged 76.
Pencil drawing (in wash); 1 in. scale; signed E.G. 18.7.24.

451 Inscription cut on Beer stone: DILIGE + DEUM / ET + FAC + QUOD + VIS.
Rubbing; $3 \times 13\frac{1}{4}$; signed E.G. 25.7.24. for Mrs. Wertheim. It is also endorsed 'Top line: black & red (alternate letters) blue "dot". Bottom line: blue with red "dots".'

452 Tombstone in memory of EDWARD COLLINS, 1854–1924.
Carved in July 1924.

453 Painted inscriptions on oak panels in memory of scholars of Brighton Grammar School who lost their lives in the Great War 1914–1918.
Work executed August 1924.

454 Inscription, surmounted by a bust of John Hunter (not E.G.'s work), on entrance to St. George's Hospital Medical School, Knightsbridge, London.
FOUNDED MDCCLII / ST. GEORGE'S HOSPITAL MEDICAL SCHOOL.
F-s. layout of portion of inscription; $4\frac{1}{2} \times 16\frac{1}{2}$; signed E.G. 5.10.24.
Architects' drawing endorsed 'H. Percy Adams, Charles Holden, Lionel G. Pearson, 9 Knightsbridge S.W.1. Sept. 26. '24'.

455 Tablet of Capel-y-ffin stone; LITTLE BELAN.
Drawing $\frac{3}{16}$ full-size; endorsed by E.G. 'Mrs. Wertheim, Stone Tab. for gate'.
Rubbing of inscription; $2 \times 15\frac{1}{2}$; signed E.G. 17.10.24.
[This rubbing bears the legend: '1st stone quarried and squared by E.G. at Capel-y-ffin.']

456 Tablet of Hopton-Wood stone, Great Easton, Dunmow, Essex, in memory of HENRY GROUT, 1852–1924.
Pencil drawing; $\frac{1}{4}$ full-size; signed E.G. 26.6.24.
Rubbing of inscription; $8\frac{1}{2} \times 19\frac{1}{2}$; signed E.G. 27.10.24.
[Henry Grout was H. G. Wells's gardener.]

457 Hopton-Wood stone tablet in Bristol Cathedral in memory of ADA VACHELL, d. 1923, Founder of The Bristol Guild of the Handicapped.
Pen and ink drawing (coloured); $\frac{1}{8}$ f-s.; signed E.G. 28.10.24. Capel-y-ffin, Abergavenny.
Full-size layout of portion of tablet; 18×25; signed E.G. Capel-y-ffin, 30.12.24.

457A The fourteen Stations of the Cross of Caen stone in the church of Our Lady and St. Peter, Leatherhead, Surrey.
These were carved by Joseph Cribb during the latter part of 1924 and early part of 1925 after drawings and specifications made by E.G.
Actual size of each Station; 20 × 18½.

458 Portland stone wall tablet, the inscription surmounted by a carving of dolphins, for an hotel in Brighton: CHARLES DICKENS 1812–1870 WAS A FREQUENT GUEST AT THIS HOTEL.
Full-size drawing; 20½ × 19; signed E.G. 24.6.24.
Rubbing; 16 × 19; signed E.G. & H.J.C.

459 Wall tablet of Portland, inscription surmounted by dolphins, on house in Brighton in which HERBERT SPENCER, 1820–1903, lived for some years.
Full-size drawing; 16 × 19; signed E.G. 24.6.24.
Rubbing; 16 × 19; signed E.G. & H.C. Jan. 1925.

460 Inscription on funeral urn of Istrian marble for WILLIAM AUGUSTUS CASSON, 1858–1924.
Rubbing of inscription; 3¾ × 13¼; signed E.G. 13.1.25. Capel-y-ffin.

461 Hopton-Wood stone tablet in the Cloisters, Westminster Abbey, in memory of Sir FREDERICK BRIDGE, C.V.O., organist of Westminster Abbey 1882–1918, born December 1844, died March 1924.
There are two pencil drawings; $\frac{1}{16}$ full-size; signed E.G. 3 & 4.7.24. Also full-size detail of lettering of portion of the inscription; 12½ × 20; signed E.G. 19.7.24.
Rubbing of inscription; 30 × 35¾; endorsed 'drawn and cut by E.G. Feb. 1925'.

462 Foundation Stone for the Whiteley Homes, Walton-on-Thames, laid 30 April, 1925 by Col. the Hon. A. G. Broderick, T.D., D.L., A.D.C., on behalf of the Trustees of the Homes.
Full-size drawing for lettering; ½ full-size; 14 × 24¼; signed E.G. for M.W. 23.4.25.

463 Memorial to WILLIAM HENRY HUDSON, 1841–1922.
'Rima' in Hyde Park, London, carved by Jacob Epstein with inscription by

E.G. This records the gift of a Bird Sanctuary dedicated to Hudson by his friends.
Work executed May 1925.
Architects' (Adams, Holden & Pearson) layout of inscription; dated April 3, 1925.

464 Headstone, with inserted panel, in memory of LOUISA CALTHROP, 1855–1925.
Pencil drawing (coloured); 1½ in. scale; signed E.G. 28.5.25.
Work executed Oct.–Nov. 1925.

465 Portland gravestone at All Saints', Corston, Bath, in memory of JULIET HELEN WEITBRECHT, 1885–1924.
Pencil sketch; ⅛ f-s.; signed E.G. 4.6.25.
There is also a drawing; ⅛ f-s.; signed E.G. 19.10.25. This is endorsed by E.G. 'For Mrs. Lionel Hoare'.
Rubbing of inscription; 43¼ × 17½; endorsed 'Drawn by E.G. cut by L.C.'.
Work executed c. 1926.

466 Headstone, surmounted by a cross, in memory of ANNIE HOUGHTON DEARLE, d. September 1923.
Pencil sketch; unsigned and undated.
Work executed June–July 1925.

467 Portland headstone, St. Michael, Wilsford, Wilts., in memory of VIOLET WATERHOUSE, eldest daughter of Sir Oliver and Lady Lodge, d. 2 January 1924 aged 36.
Pencil drawing; ⅛ full-size; signed E.G. 10.7.25.
Rubbing; 16½ × 19¾.

468 Portland headstone at Weybridge, in memory of ARTHUR CLUTTON-BROCK, 1868–1924.
Pen and ink sketch; ¾ in. scale; signed E. Gill, Capel-y-ffin. 7.4.25.
Rubbing; 28¼ × 22; signed H.J.C. for E.G. 1925.

469 Hopton-Wood stone tablet for house in Chelsea in which JOHN SINGER SARGENT R.A. (1856–1925) lived for twenty-four years and where he died 15 April, 1925.
Pencil sketch from E.G.'s hand, unsigned and undated.
Rubbing; 17½ × 35½; endorsed 'E.G. (For Prof. Tonks.) Nov. 1925'.

470 Tablet of Capel-y-ffin stone on wall over main porch of St. David's, Caldey Island, Tenby, commemorating the restoration of the church in 1925.
Rubbing; 12 × 20½; endorsed 'Laurie Cribb for E.G. Nov. 1925'.
(See also No. 512.)

471 Tablet of Capel-y-ffin stone at Brockham Green, Betchworth, Surrey, in memory of ROSINA JANE JOYCE, d. 6 May, 1924.
Pencil sketch unsigned and undated but in E.G.'s hand.
Rubbing of inscription; 12¼ × 20¼; signed E.G. del. L.C. scp. December 1925.

472 Ledger stone of Portland stone, St. Michael, Cumnor, Oxford, in memory of LILY DOUGALL, 1858–1923.
Pencil drawing; ½ full-size section of stone; signed E.G. 19.10.25.
Rubbing of inscription; 9½ × 69; signed H. J. Cribb for E.G. Jan. 1926.
(See also No. 475.)

473 Memorial in Highbury Chapel, Bristol, for HENRY ARNOLD THOMAS.
This takes the form of a carved corbel representing the Good Shepherd beneath which is the following inscription: IN MEMORY OF THE REVEREND HENRY ARNOLD THOMAS, M.A. LL.D. THE BELOVED PASTOR OF THIS CHURCH FOR 47 YRS. BORN 13 JUNE 1848 DIED 28 JUNE 1924.
There are two careful pencil drawings on 1 in. scale of alternative designs. One shows a figure of Isaiah and the other (accepted design) The Good Shepherd. Both signed E.G. 5.1.26.
F-s. drawing of inscription; 18 × 23½; signed E.G. 1.3.26.

473A Tablet of Portland stone on a wall in Black Lion Street, Brighton, inscribed: DERYK CARVER, FIRST PROTESTANT MARTYR BURNT AT LEWES JULY 22 1555. LIVED IN THIS BREWERY.
This is now part of Fremlin's Brewery adjoining the Cricketers' Arms Hotel.
Rubbing; 14 × 30; dated May 1926.
[This work was commissioned by the Brighton Town Council.]

474 Headstone of Portland stone in St. Giles Cemetery, Huntingdon Road, Cambridge, in memory of FRANCIS DARWIN, 1848–1925.
Pencil drawing; 1 in. scale; signed E.G. 14.12.25. Capel-y-ffin.
Rubbing; 15 × 17; signed E.G. del. L.C. scp. June 1926.

475 Hopton-Wood stone tablet in S. transept, St. Michael, Cumnor, Oxford, in memory of LILY DOUGALL, 1858–1923.
Pencil sketch of lettering; ½ full-size; (unsigned).
Pen and ink drawing; ⅛ f-s.; signed E.G. 14.6.26.
Rubbing of inscription; 21¾ × 16¼; signed 'E.G., del. L. Cribb, sc. October 1926'.
(See also No. 472.)

476 Gravestone of Portland stone in memory of HELEN THORP AND JOSEPH PETER THORP.
Pencil drawing; signed E.G. 23.7.23.
Rubbing; 15½ × 16¼; endorsed 'Portland Stone. Drawn & cut by E.G. Nov. 1926.'

477 Hopton-Wood stone tablet in Fisher Hall, Cambridge, in memory of PERCY FITZGERALD, d. 1925.
Pen and ink drawing; ⅛ f-s.; signed E.G. Capel-y-ffin, 25.5.26.
Rubbing of inscription; 25 × 30; endorsed 'Drawn on stone by E.G., cut by Laurence Cribb, July 1926. For the Cambridge Catholic Association'.

478 Recumbent gravestone, St. Nicholas, Brushford, Dulverton, Somerset, in memory of AUBREY HERBERT, M.P., Captain Irish Guards, 1880–1923. Son of Henry, 4th Earl of Caernarvon.
Pen and ink drawings; $\frac{1}{12}$ f-s. approx.; signed E.G. 23.8.26.

479 Wooden panel with words painted in red and black, from Saint Thomas Aquinas: 'La Beauté / Divine est cause de / l'être de tout ce qui est. The Beauty of God is the / cause of the being of all that is.' The French in roman caps, in black, alternating with the English in upper & l.c. italics, in red.
Size of panel; 22 × 30.
[This was for the V. & A. Museum's Circulation Department for their travelling exhibitions. They also published a collotype reproduction in 1926 as No. 4 of four Lettering Sheets.]

479A Hopton-Wood stone panel with Roman capitals, incised and coloured, of a quotation from Saint Thomas Aquinas: EX DIVINA PVLCHRITV-DINE ESSE OMNIUM DERIVATVR.
Rubbing; 14½ × 20½; signed E.G. August 1926.

[This was done for the Victoria & Albert Museum's Circulation Department for their travelling exhibitions.]

[The Museum published a collotype reproduction of it (the letters in red, black and blue) in 1936 as No. 3 of four Lettering Sheets.]

480 Foundation stone for the College Chapel, St. Oswald's, Ellesmere College, Salop.
Full-size drawing; $29\frac{3}{4} \times 41\frac{1}{2}$; signed E.G. 20.9.26.
Rubbing; $27\frac{1}{2} \times 39\frac{1}{2}$; signed L.C. for E.G. Sept. 1926.

481 Hopton-Wood headstone at Packwood Haugh, Lapworth, Warwickshire, in memory of FLORENCE BRADSHAW, d. 1925.
Pencil drawing (coloured); $1\frac{1}{2}$ in. scale; signed E.G. 25.5.26.
Rubbing of inscription; $17\frac{1}{2} \times 20\frac{1}{2}$; signed E.G. & L.C. del. L.C.Sc. Sep. '26.
(See also No. 500.)

482 Portland headstone at Weybridge, in memory of JOHN ALAN CLUTTON-BROCK, 1842–1925.
Pencil drawing (tinted); $\frac{1}{12}$ f-s.; signed E.G. 28.7.26.
Rubbing; $18 \times 20\frac{1}{2}$; signed E.G. del. L.C. sep. Nov. 1926.

483 Headstone of Portland stone, in memory of WILLIAM STEPHEN MARCHANT, 1870–1925.
Pencil drawings (tinted); 1 in. scale; signed E.G. 23.2.26 and 25.3.26.

484 Fascia board lettered DOUGLAS CLEVERDON for bookshop formerly in Park Street, Bristol, painted by E.G. Oct. 30–Nov. 1, 1926. This was destroyed in an air raid during World War II.
[From the letters used on this board the type design we know as *Gill Sans* was developed in 1927. A photograph of the board appears in *An Approach to Type*, by J. R. Biggs. London: Blandford Press, 1949, p. 42.]
(See also No. 484A.) [*See Plate XVI*]

484A Zinc name-plate: originally placed above the bell-push at Douglas Cleverdon's bookshop in Bristol which was destroyed in an air raid.
Rubbing; $2 \times 4\frac{1}{2}$; November 1926.
[A reproduction of this rubbing will be found in *The Monotype Recorder*, Vol. 41, No. 3, 1958, p. 15.]
(See also No. 484.)

485 Brass tablet on W. wall of the ante-chapel Eton College, Windsor, with Coat of Arms and inscription in Latin, letters engraved and filled in with black and red wax, in memory of LVDOVICVS HEATHCOAT AMORY of Tiverton, killed in action in France 24 August 1918, aged 37.
Pencil drawing; $6\frac{1}{2} \times 16\frac{3}{4}$; signed E.G. Capel-y-ffin. 8.11.26.

486 Tablet in the Crypt Chapel, Downside Abbey, Bath, in memory of EVERARD GREEN, 1844–1926. He was appointed Rouge Dragon Pursuivant of Arms 10 March 1893 and became Somerset Herald in 1911.
Work executed c. 1926.

487 Letter-box cover with the word LETTERS (these letters are set one beneath the other) carved in wood for the house '4 Elms', Waltham St. Lawrence, Berks., occupied by Robert and Moira Gibbings, owners of the Golden Cockerel Press.
Above the door is a stone-carving by E.G. depicting four elms and embodying the initials 'R & M.G'.
Rubbing of inscription; $7 \times \frac{3}{4}$; endorsed by E.G. 'Cut by L.C.'
Work executed c. 1926.

487A Foundation stone for Torbay Hospital laid by Mrs. Ella Marian Rowcroft, 26 June 1926.
Rubbing; $22\frac{1}{4} \times 48$; dated 1926.
(See also No. 514A.)

488 Hopton-Wood stone tablet in memory of ANNE ELIZABETH CHANCE, d. October 1925.
Pen and ink drawing (in red and black); $2\frac{1}{4}$ in. scale; signed E.G. Capel-y-ffin, 31.7.26.
Rubbing of inscription; $15 \times 12\frac{3}{4}$; signed L.C. for E.G. January 1927.

489 Headstone, the inscription surmounted by a crucifix, at Harlow, Essex, in memory of MARIA ANNA GILBEY, 1897–1927 of Mark Hall (Harlow).
Pencil sketch; unsigned, together with a pencil and wash drawing; $\frac{1}{8}$ scale signed; E.G. 7.3.27.

490 Memorial panel of Hopton-Wood stone for All Saints, Pimlico, London, in memory of AMBROSE McEVOY, 1878–1927.
Full-size layout of letters; $7\frac{3}{4} \times 21\frac{1}{4}$; signed E.G. 13.3.27.
Pen and ink sketch; signed E.G. Ap. 1927.

Rubbing; $8\frac{3}{4} \times 22\frac{1}{4}$.

[This memorial was destroyed when the church was bombed during the 1939–1945 war.]

491 Tablet in memory of Major NICHOLAS ROTHESAY MONTAGUE STUART WORTLEY, M.C., Royal Flying Corps, 1892–1926.
Pen and ink sketch; signed E.G. Ap. 1927.

491A Foundation stone for the ROYAL WESTMINSTER OPHTHALMIC HOSPITAL, High Holborn, London W.C.1. This stone was laid by H.R.H. the Duke of Connaught K.G. 30th June 1927.
Pencil drawing; signed E.G. 4.6.27. Dimensions: 20 × 30.
[This is now the Holborn branch of the Moorfields Eye Hospital.]

492 Hopton-Wood stone tablet in memory of FRANK WILLIAM ALBION GODFREY, M.B., C.M. Edin., 1860–1925.
A pencil drawing; $1\frac{1}{2}$ scale; signed 'E.G. 1.6.27.' is endorsed 'discarded'. There is a tablet from another design; full-size drawing of portion of inscription and rubbing; $25 \times 41\frac{3}{4}$. This is undated and unsigned.

493 Portland stone tablet, the inscription surmounted by dolphins, on house in Brighton, in memory of AUBREY BEARDSLEY, 1872–1898, who was born in that house.
Pencil sketch and full-size drawing; both signed E.G. 2.7.27.
Rubbing; $21\frac{3}{4} \times 18\frac{3}{4}$; endorsed 'H. J. Cribb for E. Gill, 20.viii.27.'

494 Portland stone tablet, in Brighton, the inscription surmounted by dolphins, on Brighton Grammar School, in memory of E. J. MARSHALL, Headmaster of the school 1861–1899, d. 1899.
Pencil sketch and full-size drawing; both signed E.G. 2.7.27.
Rubbing; $21\frac{3}{4} \times 18\frac{3}{4}$; endorsed 'H. J. Cribb for E. Gill, 20.viii.27.'

495 War memorial tablet worked in black marble, in the entrance hall of the offices of Crosse & Blackwell, Ltd. in Soho Square, London. This commemorates the members of the staff who lost their lives in the Great War 1914–1918.
Rubbing of inscription; 24 × 66; signed L.C. sc., E.G. del. July 1927.
[This memorial, recording some thirty-seven names, though still in existence has been covered by an oak tablet on which are inscribed the names of those who fell in both the 1914–18 and 1939–45 wars.]

496 Tablet of Hopton-Wood stone, St. Michael's Howick, Alnwick, Northumberland, in memory of VICTORIA SYBIL MARY GRENFELL, 1878–1907, daughter of 4th Earl Grey.
Pen and ink drawing; $\frac{1}{8}$ f-s.; signed E.G. 28.7.26.
Rubbing of inscription; $19\frac{1}{4} \times 28$; signed E.G. del. L.C. scp.

497 Portland headstone on White Nose cliff, Lulworth Cove, Dorset, in memory of WALTER FRANZEN, d. May 1927. aged 34.
Pencil drawing; $\frac{1}{8}$ full-size; signed E.G. 16.8.27.

498 Alphabet of capital letters incised on Hopton-Wood stone, for the Victoria & Albert Museum, London.
Rubbing; $19\frac{1}{2} \times 21$; endorsed 'For S.K.M., E.G. del; L.C. & E.G. Sc. Aug. 1927'.

498A Alphabet of 3 in. capital letters in relief on Hopton-Wood stone, for the Victoria & Albert Museum, London.
Rubbing; $19\frac{3}{4} \times 20\frac{3}{4}$; endorsed 'For S.K.M., E.G. del; L.C. & E.G. Sc. Aug. 1927'.

499 Portland headstone in Compton Cemetery, Guildford, Surrey, in memory of ETHEL ANN BURTON-BROWN, of Friars Field, 1868–1927.
Pencil sketch; signed E.G. 10.5.27.
Pencil drawing; $\frac{1}{8}$ full-size; signed E.G. Capel-y-ffin 1.6.27.
Full-size drawing of portion of headstone (undated).
Rubbing; $33\frac{1}{2} \times 27$; signed E.G. 1.9.27.

500 Tablet of Portland stone, at Packwood Haugh, Lapworth, Warwickshire, the inscription surmounted by a panel of the Madonna and child in relief, in memory of FLORENCE BRADSHAW, 1895–1922.
Full-size detail; $26\frac{1}{2} \times 13\frac{1}{4}$; signed E.G. 1.9.27.
(See also No. 481.)

501 War Memorial tablet of Hopton-Wood stone St. Michael and All Angels', Sopley, Hants, commemorating the restoration of the belfry and bells in 1927 and in memory of those who gave their lives in the Great War, 1914–1918.
Size of tablet; 33×34.
Pen and ink sketch; $\frac{1}{8}$ f-s.; signed E.G. 22.10.27.

502 Wall tablet, the inscription surmounted by dolphins, on a house in Burlington Street, Brighton, commemorating GEORGE CANNING, Statesman, 1770–1827, who at one time lived there.
Rubbing; 17¾ × 20; signed H. J. Cribb, 1927.

503 Tablet for house formerly at 60 Sidney Street, Cambridge, where CHARLES DARWIN lived in 1828.
This tablet (7¼ × 16½) was placed in the Folk Museum, Cambridge, when the house was destroyed.
Rubbing; unsigned and undated.
Tablet carved c. 1927.
(See also No. 504.)

504 Tablet for house 22 Fitzwilliam Street, Cambridge, where CHARLES DARWIN lived 1836–37.
Rubbing of inscription; 8¾ × 17½; c. 1927.
(See also No. 503.)

505 Headstone in memory of Lieut.-Col. E. A. BALL, late Royal Warwickshire Regiment, 1848–1926.
Work executed January–February 1928.
[There are two pencil sketches; both unsigned and undated. In his diary under date of 16 July 1927 E.G. recorded this drawing and under 26 January 1928 he records having begun the carving.]

506 Memorial tablet of Hopton-Wood stone in memory of JOHN BEAUMONT HOTHAM of Milne Graden, nr. Coldstream, Berwickshire, 1874–1924. After twenty-three years' service in the House of Lords he was appointed Clerk of the Senate in the first Parliament of Northern Ireland, 1921–1924.
Pencil drawing $\frac{1}{12}$ full-size; signed E.G. 12.7.27. And another pencil drawing $\frac{1}{8}$ full-size; signed E.G. 19.8.27. There is also a full-size specimen of the incised letters; signed E.G. 12.7.27.
Rubbing of inscription; 29 × 18¾; signed E.G. del., L.C. sc.

507 Head and footstone in memory of ANGELA GILBEY, d. April 1925.
Full-size detail of decoration and cornice; signed E.G. 1.9.27.
Rubbing of inscription; 16¼ × 21; signed E.G. del., L.C. sc. March 1928.

508 Wall tablet, inscription surmounted by Coat of Arms, St. Peter, Stourton, Wilts., in memory of AYLEN DE TAVORA LUIS DE FERNANDES, 1902–1921.

Pencil drawing of tablet together with full-size layout of portion of the inscription (which is surmounted by three Coats of Arms); $18 \times 18\frac{1}{2}$; both signed E.G. 28.3.28.

There is also a pen and ink sketch of the Fernandes Arms.

509 Tablet of Hopton-Wood stone, St. Nicholas, Poling nr. Arundel, in memory of Sir HARRY JOHNSTON, G.C.M.G., K.C.B., D.Sc., Administrator, Soldier, Explorer and Naturalist, 1858–1927.

Pen and ink drawing; $\frac{1}{8}$ full-size; unsigned but endorsed in E.G.'s hand 'circa Sept. 1927'.

Rubbing of inscription; $14 \times 19\frac{1}{4}$; signed E.G. del., L.C. sc., April 1928.

510 Portland headstone, surmounted by a crucifix, at Garstang, Lancs., in memory of MARY REEVES, d. 18 May 1927 aged 67 years.

Pencil drawing; $1\frac{1}{8}$ in. scale; signed E.G. 16.8.27.

Full-size layout of inscription; $18\frac{1}{4} \times 11\frac{1}{4}$; signed E.G. 25.4.28. There is also a pencil drawing of a female figure, for the back of the headstone, signed E.G. 24.4.28.

511 Gravestone of Hopton-Wood stone in Bradford Cemetery in memory of CHARLES LAMBERT RUTHERSTON, 1866–1927, son of Moritz and Bertha Rothenstein.

Pencil drawing; $\frac{1}{12}$ full-size; signed E.G. 27.3.28.

Detailed drawing of portion of gravestone; signed E.G., 14.5.28.

Rubbing; 14×16; signed E.G. del, L.C.sc. July 1928.

512 Bath stone font in St. David's, Caldey Island, Tenby, with inscription: NON POTEST INTRARE IN REGNUM COELORUM ... (St. John, 3, v.).

Full-size plan of base; 30×30; signed E.G. 29.7.28.

(See also No. 470.)

513 Carved crucifix on headstone (Portland stone) 4 ft. 7 in. high, in the graveyard of the Catholic Church of St. Edmund, Abingdon, in memory of MONTAGU ARTHUR 7th Earl of Abingdon, 1836–1928. High Steward of Abingdon.

There are two pencil drawings (coloured), for alternative designs; both signed E.G. 8.11.28.

Rubbing of portion of inscription; $9\frac{1}{2} \times 41\frac{1}{2}$; signed E.G. del., H.J.C. scpt. June 1929.

514 Circular tablet of Portland stone, letters in relief: B B C (British Broadcasting Company).

The title was changed to 'British Broadcasting Corporation' in January 1927. This tablet was on the outside wall of the original headquarters of the British Broadcasting Corporation in Savoy Hill, London.

Rubbing; $17\frac{1}{2} \times 16\frac{1}{4}$; 1928.

514A Panel of Hopton-Wood stone in Torbay Hospital recording the gratitude of the Governors to Mrs. Ella Marian Rowcroft of Pilmuir, Torquay, for the gift of the hospital and Nurse's Home.

Work executed in 1928.

(See also No. 487A.)

515 Hopton-Wood head and foot-stone (near Oxford) in memory of FRANCIS ELRINGTON BALL, Litt.D., d. January 1928. Also of FLORENCE EGLANTINE his wife, d. August 1913.

There are three pencil drawings; $1\frac{1}{2}$ in. scale; signed E.G. and bearing dates in February and March 1929.

516 Bronze tablet in the ante-chapel of Balliol College, Oxford, in memory of HENRY HERBERT ASQUITH, Earl of Oxford & Asquith, 1852–1928.

Full-size drawing of lettering; $13\frac{3}{4} \times 28$; signed E.G. 12.2.29.

517 Ledger stone outside South transept of Peterborough Cathedral in memory of JOHN EDWARD STOCKS, 1843–1926. Canon of Peterborough.

Drawings of lettering; signed E.G. 28.3.29 & 30.3.29.

518 Foundation stone and inscription on stone over main entrance of the headquarters of the London Underground Railways, St. James's Park Station, Broadway, Westminster. March 1929.

The letter-cutting was the joint work of E.G. and Laurie Cribb.

519 Hopton-Wood stone tablet in a Library at Tirana, Albania, commemorating the gift of the library to the young people of Albania. The inscription runs: HANC BIBLIOTHECAM IN USUM POPULI ALBANI AEDIFICANDAM CURAVIT ELISABETHA COMTISSA DE CARNARVON. MANET IN MEMORIAM ET MATRIS . . . 1929.

Pencil drawing; signed E.G. 22.3.29.

Rubbing of inscription; $15\frac{3}{4} \times 21\frac{3}{4}$; signed E.G. del., L.C., sc. Ap. 1929.

(See also No. 565.)

520 Designs for face and gnomon of a sundial in Whitley, Surrey.
Full-size drawing and lettering on face; $27\frac{3}{4} \times 27\frac{1}{2}$; signed E. G. Piggotts,
North Dean, High Wycombe 30.4.29.
Design for gnomon; 15×10; unsigned.
Architects' (Sir Aston Webb & Son) plan; dated October 1928.

521 Portland headstone in Stanmer Park, nr. Brighton, in memory of
JOCELYN BRUDENELL PELHAM, 6th Earl of Chichester. b. 1871,
d. 14 November 1926, also of FRANCIS GODOLPHIN HENRY
PELHAM, 7th Earl, b. 1904 d. 22 November 1926.
 The back of this stone carries an inscription: 'All shall be well . . .' from
Revelations of Divine Love by Julian of Norwich.
Two pencil drawings of headstone both $\frac{1}{12}$ f-s.; signed E.G. 27.12.28.; and
of inscription on the back signed E.G. 23.6.29.
Rubbing of inscription on back of headstone; 15×18; signed E.G. del. L.C Sc.,
July 1929.

522 Memorial of Hopton-Wood stone, in Brompton Cemetery, London, in
memory of HELEN ROSE, 1894–1928 also of FREDERICK LEOPOLD,
Lieut. Irish Guards, D.S.O., killed in action at Loos 27 June 1916, aged 20
and of ERNEST JOHN, 2nd Lieut. Royal Warwickshire Regt., killed in
action on the Somme 8 August 1916. The children of Emile and Helen Pusch.
Pencil drawing; signed E.G. 16.2.29.
Rubbing of inscription at base of the memorial; $4\frac{1}{2} \times 49\frac{1}{2}$; signed E.G. del.,
L.C. scp. June 1929. (An additional inscription was cut in 1940.)

523 Portland headstone in Brompton Cemetery, London, in memory of
EMILY ALICE WHITE. 1845–1922.
Pencil sketch; signed E.G. 1.7.29.
Pencil drawing; 1 in. scale; signed E.G. 8.8.23.
Rubbing of inscription; $22 \times 25\frac{1}{2}$; 1929.
A further inscription was added in 1932.

524 Exhibition piece—TU ES PETRUS ET SUPER . . .
Rubbing; 12×21; unsigned and undated; *c.* 1929.

525 Wall tablet of Hopton-Wood stone, inscription surmounted by dolphins,
on house in Brighton in which GIDEON ALGERNON MANTELL,
Geologist, lived 1833–38.
Rubbing; $22\frac{1}{4} \times 18\frac{1}{4}$; signed E.G. del., L.C. sc. Aug. 1929.

526 Cruciform headstone in memory of COLVILLE ADRIAN DE RUNE BARCLAY, 1869–1929.
Pencil and wash drawing of cross; 1 in. scale; signed E.G. 12.8.29.
An additional inscription was cut by Laurie Cribb in May 1930.

527 Headstone in Bristol in memory of KOSSUTH ROBINSON, d. February 1928 and of his three sons, CLIFFORD KOSSUTH, EDWARD COLSTON and GEOFFREY WATHEN who were killed in the Great War, 1915.
Pencil drawing; signed E.G. 12.8.29.
Actual size of headstone; 63 × 34.

528 Cruciform gravestone in the Extramural cemetery, Brighton (the inscription cut in Sans-serif letters), in memory of CICELEY ROSE GILL, 1854–1929, wife of the Revd. Arthur T. Gill.
Full-size setting-out, filled in black, of letters; signed E.G. 21.8.29.
Full-size setting-out in pencil of the letters CICELY ROSE on base of cross; $1\frac{1}{8} \times 10\frac{1}{2}$; signed E.G.
A further inscription was added in 1933 commemorating the Revd. ARTHUR TIDMAN GILL, 1848–1933.
[This stone commemorates Eric Gill's parents.]

529 Headstone of Portland stone, with figure of a child carved in relief, in memory of JOHNNIE MANN, d. 28 November 1925, aged $4\frac{1}{2}$ years.
Pencil sketch and drawing both $\frac{1}{8}$ full-size, both signed E.G. 8.9.28.
Outline key drawing; $\frac{1}{8}$ full-size to depths of cutting; signed E.G. 1.2.29.

530 Head and footstones of Portland stone in Brookwood Cemetery, Woking, in memory of HENRI SEE, 1862–1929 and another in memory of MAY SEE, d. 1880.
Pencil drawing (tinted); $\frac{1}{12}$ full-size; signed E.G. 27.7.29.
Rubbing of inscriptions; $8\frac{1}{2} \times 16\frac{1}{2}$ and $5\frac{1}{4} \times 15\frac{1}{4}$ respectively; signed E.G. del., L.C.sc. Nov. 1929.

531 Gravestone on Rogoa Island, off Samarai, Papua, in memory of FRANCES MARY GILL, born 1 July 1926, died 19 May 1929. Daughter of Cecil and Nonie Gill.
Pencil sketch by E.G. unsigned and undated.
Actual size of gravestone; $14\frac{1}{2} \times 15$.
Work executed December 1929.

531A Carved headboard of an oak bed in Cambridge, Mass., U.S.A. This consists of three panels each containing a carving in relief with incised lettering above and beneath each carving. Left-hand panel inscribed: HIC NATI PER DOLORES AD CAPIENDA PER PARTVM VIRGINIS GAVDIA INENNARABILIA. Centre: HIC RENOVATVR IN AMORE SPONSALI GENVS HOMINVM MORTALE PER SPON-SALIA CHRISTI ET ECCLESIA MIRIFICA COELICOLARVM IMMORTALE. Right-hand panel: HIC TANDEM OBRIGESCIMVS MORTE POENA PECCATI PER ADAE CVLPAM: PER RESVRRECTIONXTI PORTA SOLA VITE.

The two outside panels; $12 \times 10\frac{1}{2}$, the centre panel; $12\frac{1}{2} \times 14\frac{1}{2}$. The relief carvings were done by E.G. at Capel-y-ffin. The bed was made by Romney Green in whose workshop at Christchurch, Hants, the inscriptions were also cut from drawings sent to him by E.G.

[This was commissioned by Graham Carey, Cambridge, Mass., and executed late in 1929.]

532 Headstone of Portland stone in memory of ARTHUR STANSFIELD DIXON of Birmingham, 1856–1929. Also of his children MARY DIXON, 1887–1922 and JAMES EVELYN DIXON, 1893–1916, killed in action at Beaumont Hamel, 1 July 1916.

Rubbing of work executed 1929.

532A Inscriptions, incised on York stone, on building in Chichester Rents, Chancery Lane, London, W.C.2.: CHICHESTER and CHICHESTER ESTATES CO.

Rubbings; $2 \times 12\frac{3}{4}$ and $3\frac{1}{2} \times 11\frac{3}{4}$ respectively; endorsed Prudence Pelham del. & sc. 1930.

533 Altar tombstone with inscriptions on two sides, and foliage at each end, at Little Compton, Moreton-in-the-Marsh, Glos., in memory of FREDERICK LEVERTON HARRIS, P.C., 1864–1927.

Pencil sketch of tombstone; signed E.G. Jan 1930.

Full-size drawing of $3\frac{1}{2}$ in. letters and figures to be cut; signed E.G. 21.6.30.

Rubbing of inscription on one side $11 \times 62\frac{1}{2}$ and of the other side $11 \times 62\frac{1}{4}$; both unsigned and undated.

There is a sketch for an additional inscription in memory of GERTRUDE, wife of the above, d. Dec. 1938; signed E.G. 23.10.38.

534 Hopton-Wood stone tablet in memory of HENRY HILL HICKMAN 1800–1830. Died at Tenbury.

Pencil sketch; $\frac{1}{8}$ f-s.; signed E.G. 17.3.30.

This is inscribed: THIS TABLET IS PLACED HERE AT THE INITIATIVE OF THE SECTION OF ANAESTHETICS OF THE ROYAL SOCIETY OF MEDICINE AS A CENTENARY TRIBUTE TO THE MEMORY OF THE EARLIEST KNOWN PIONEER OF ANAESTHESIA BY INHALATION.

Rubbing; $33 \times 28\frac{1}{2}$; signed E.G. del. L.C. sc. March 1930.

535 Portland ledger-stone in Kensal Green Cemetery, London, in memory of ANTONII POLIMENI, 1844–1928.

Pencil drawing; $\frac{1}{4}$ f-s. of portion of inscription; signed E.G. 28.2.30.

Rubbings of inscriptions; on side of stone 12×73, and on foot $7\frac{3}{4} \times 10\frac{1}{2}$; both signed E.G. del. L.C. sc. May 1930.

536 Hopton-Wood stone tablet in memory of CHARLES FREDERICK GURNEY MASTERMAN, 1873–1927.

Pencil drawing; $\frac{1}{8}$ f-s.; signed E.G. 10.5.29.

Rubbing; $34\frac{1}{2} \times 25\frac{1}{4}$; undated.

Work executed March 1930.

[This memorial was originally erected in St. Stephen's Church, Walworth, which was destroyed by enemy action during World War II. It was re-erected in St. George's Church, Camberwell, and re-dedicated October 24, 1961.]

537 Ledger-stone of Portland stone, St. Michael and All Angels, Himley, Dudley, Staffs., in memory of JOHN JEREMY WARD, 1922–1929.

[This commemorates a child of the Dudley family.]

Pencil drawing; $\frac{1}{8}$ f-s.; signed E.G. 20.3.1930.

Rubbing of inscription; $42\frac{3}{4} \times 20\frac{1}{2}$; unsigned and undated.

538 Carving in the main porch St. Mary's, Liss, Hants. (the porch designed by Sir Edward Maufe).

The carving is a figure of the Christ Child (about 2 ft. 3 in. high) with inscription: IN GLORIAM DEI MEMORIAM QUE SARAH GABBATT MATRIS DILECTISSIMAE FILIA FILIUSQUE HANC PORTICUM EXSTRANDUM CURAVERUNT MCMXXX.

This work was executed 1930–31.

(See also No. 538A.)

538A Tablet on triple gravestone, on N. side of the churchyard, St. Mary, Liss, Hants., in memory of SARAH GABBATT, b. 27 Sept. 1853, d. 22 Dec. 1929.
This is the left-hand tablet of three, the centre one of which is surmounted by a cross on the base of which is inscribed ☧.
The work was carried out c. 1930.

539 Cruciform headstone, the inscription surmounted by a crucifix, in memory of LOUISA ANNIE GRAY, 1860–1929.
Pencil drawing; $\frac{1}{8}$ full-size; signed E.G. 30.5.30.

540 Signboard of painted letters: TAXIDERMIST.
This was done for exhibition purposes and is in Department of Circulation, Victoria & Albert Museum, London.
Size of board; 15 × 90; May 1930.

541 Tablet of polished Hopton-Wood stone, on N. wall St. James, Piccadilly, London, in memory of MARY BEATRICE JOHNSON, 1857–1929.
Pen and ink drawing; approx. $\frac{1}{8}$ f-s.; letters in red and black; signed E.G. 17.12.29.
Rubbing; signed E.G. del., L.C.sc. May 1930.
Actual size of tablet; $17\frac{1}{2} \times 22\frac{1}{4}$.

542 Hopton-Wood stone tablet in the private chapel at Rycote, Thame, Oxon., in memory of ALFRED ST. GEORGE HAMERSLEY, 1848–1929.
Pen and ink drawing; $\frac{1}{8}$ f-s.; signed E.G. 17.2.30.
Rubbing of inscription; $12\frac{3}{4} \times 29\frac{1}{2}$; signed E.G.del., L.C. sc. June 1930.
[The tablet was 'signed' E.G. (at Miss C. Hamersley's request) and is thus one of the few inscriptional works 'signed' by him.]
(See also No. 543.)

543 Brass tablet with inscription and Coat of Arms, St. Mary, Pyrton, Wallingford, in memory of ALFRED ST. GEORGE HAMERSLEY, 1848–1929.
Pen and ink drawing (coloured); $\frac{1}{8}$ f-s.; signed E.G. 17.2.30.
Rubbing of tablet; $28\frac{3}{4} \times 29\frac{3}{4}$; signed E.G. del., L.C.sc. June 1930.
(See also No. 542.)

544 Gravestone worked in York stone, St. Michael and All Angels, Himley, Dudley, Staffs., in memory of GEORGINA, Countess of DUDLEY, 1846–1929.
Rubbing of inscription; $39\frac{1}{4} \times 19\frac{1}{2}$; signed L.C. sc., E.G. del. June, 1930.

545 Tablet in the ante-chapel, New College, Oxford, in memory of German Nationals, men of the College, who fought and died for their country, 1914–1918: PRINZ WOLRAD-FRIEDRICH ZU WALDECK-PYRMOUNT: FREIHERR WILHELM VON SELL: ERWIN BEIT VON SPEYER.
Pencil drawing; $\frac{1}{4}$ full-size; carrying at foot the names of the architects, Adams, Holden & Pearson.
Rubbing of tablet; $12\frac{3}{4} \times 58$; work executed 1930.
Laurie Cribb assisted in the cutting of the inscription.
(See also No. 398.)

546 Gravestone in the churchard, St. James the Apostle, Bushey, Herts., in memory of JOHN SAXON MILLS, M.A., Barrister-at-Law, d. Nov. 26. 1929.
This is followed by an inscription in Greek letters.
Pencil drawing, showing 2 in. letters; signed E.G. 11.8.30.
Actual size of gravestone; $41\frac{1}{2} \times 18$.

547 Inscriptions, incised and gilded, on bases of black marble candelabra in St. George's Chapel, Windsor, recording the gift by King George V and Queen Mary in memory of KING EDWARD VII and QUEEN ALEXANDRA.
Drawing; 4×20; signed E.G. 16.8.30.
Rubbings; $3\frac{3}{4} \times 21\frac{1}{4}$ and $4 \times 20\frac{3}{4}$; signed H.J.C[ribb] for E.G. 1930.

548 Headstone at Clovelly, Devon, the inscription surmounted by a carving of Christ the King, with His Mother, and St. Mary Magdalen, on either side, in memory of SIBELL MARGARET LUMLEY, born 1855, at Tickell, married 1874 Victor Alexander, Earl Grosvenor. Secondly she married George Wyndham, M.P. She died at Saighton Grange, Feb 4, 1929.
The inscription embodies three shields.
Size of memorial; 103×124; pencil drawing (tinted); signed E.G.1.9.30.
F-s. pencil drawing of portion of inscription, showing 4 in. letters and position of the Lumley shield; signed E.G. 1.9.30.

549 Ledger stone of York stone, St. Michael and All Angels, Himley, Dudley, Staffs., in memory of ROSEMARY MILLICENT, Viscountess EDNAM, 1893–1930.
Rubbing; $42\frac{1}{2} \times 20\frac{1}{2}$; signed E.G. del.; L.C. sc. September 1930.

550 Tablet of Hopton-Wood stone in Fairbairn House, Barking Road, Plaistow, London, E.13, commemorating the gift of the first Fairbairn House opened in 1900 as the Boys Club of Mansfield House University Settlement.
Pencil drawing; $\frac{1}{8}$ full-size; signed E.G. 20.11.30.
Rubbing of inscription for central panel; $15\frac{1}{4} \times 64\frac{1}{2}$, and of the two side panels; $17\frac{3}{4} \times 19\frac{3}{4}$; signed E.G. del. L.C. scp. Feb. 1931.

551 Hopton-Wood stone tablet, inscription surmounted by dolphins, on house in Brighton in which FREDERICK WILLIAM ROBERTSON lived, 1847–1850.
Rubbing of tablet; $18\frac{3}{4} \times 23\frac{3}{4}$; signed E.G. del., L.C. scp. Dec., 1930.

552 Tablet of Hopton-Wood stone in St. Mary's Leigh Woods, Bristol, in memory of JOHN GAMBLE, B.D., 1859–1929. Canon of Bristol.
Pen and ink drawing letters in red and black, $\frac{1}{8}$ full-size; signed E.G. 9.6.30.
Rubbing of inscription; $30 \times 17\frac{1}{2}$; signed E.G. del. L.C. sc. December 1930.

553 Incised cap. and lower-case letters on Hopton-Wood stone: VOX DILECTI MEI ECCE ISTE VENIT / The voice of my beloved, behold he comes leaping / SALIENS IN MONTIBUS TRANSILIENS COLLES / upon the mountains and skipping upon the hills.
Rubbing of inscription; $6\frac{3}{4} \times 36\frac{1}{2}$; endorsed 'Prudence P[elham] and E.G. del. PP. sc. 1930 (HW stone)'.

554 Brass plate showing Coat of Arms and inscription in memory of ANN, daughter of Sir Richard FANSHAWE, who died at Tankersley Park, Barnsley, Yorks., 22nd July, 1654.
Rubbing of plate; $6\frac{1}{4} \times 9$; [n.d.] c. 1930.

555 Oval tablet of Hopton-Wood stone, S. Michael and All Angels, Tenbury Wells, Worcs., in memory of SIR BENJAMIN BROWNE & ANNIE his wife, who were married in this church, February 9, 1861.
Pen and ink drawing, letters in red and black; signed E.G. Pigotts, N. Dean, High Wycombe, 20.3.30.
Rubbing; 36×30; signed E.G. inv. et del. L.C. sc. Jan. 1931.

556 Cruciform headstone of Portland stone in the private cemetery, St. George's Retreat, Burgess Hill, Sussex, in memory of ROMOLA MARY TRENCH, 1895–1930.
Inscription in Italian surmounted by a crucifix.
Pencil and wash drawing; 1 in. scale; signed E.G. 9.8.30.
Rubbing of inscription; 16½ × 8; signed E.G. del. L.C. sc. Jan. 1931.

557 Hopton-Wood stone tablet in the library of the Royal Automobile Club, Pall Mall, London, in memory of GEORGE CHARLES ASHTON-JONSON, Hon. Librarian of the Club.
Pen and ink drawings; 2 in. scale; numbered 1 & 2; signed E.G. 3.12.30.
Rubbing; 9 × 12; signed E.G. del., L.C. sc. Jan. '31.

557A Inscription: ECCE ABSORBEBIT FLVVIVM ET NON . . .
Pen and ink sketch (with an English translation).
It is not known whether or not this job was executed; the sketch, though unsigned, is from E.G.'s hand and dated by him 15.1.31.

558 Pillar of Clipsham stone, about 7 ft. high, to west of Grove Buildings, Merton College, Oxford, in memory of ANDREW COMYN IRVINE, 1902–1924, who lost his life on Mt. Everest.
Pencil drawing, tinted; signed E.G. 6.2.31.

559 Inscription on Portland stone on Lych Gate, Westdean, Seaford, Sussex, in memory of EVELYN JAMES.
Pen and ink sketch of lettering and two figures; by E.G.'s hand but neither signed nor dated.
Rubbing of inscription; 16 × 81; signed E.G. & H.J.C. del., H.J.C. scp., February, 1931.

560 Tombstone of Clipsham stone in St. George's Chapel, Windsor, in memory of LOUISE MARGARET ALEXANDRA VICTORIA AGNES, third daughter of H.R.H. Prince Frederick Charles of Prussia, 1860–1917, Duchess of Connaught.
Pencil sketch showing layout; unsigned and undated.
Rubbing of portion of inscription; in 2 in. letters; signed E.G. del., L.C., scp. Spring, 1931.

561 Gravestone in York stone, St. Mary Denham, Bucks., in memory of RICHARD HENRY MORTEN, 1858–1930, of Hill's House, Denham.
Rubbing of inscription; 23¼ × 18¾; signed E.G. del., L.C., sc., March, 1931.

562 Brass tablet, the inscription in 1 in. caps, surmounted by the figure of a bishop, in St. Mary's, Cadogan Gardens, London, in memory of JOANNI BIDWELL, C.B.E., D.D., 1872–1930.

Pen and ink drawing (coloured); $\frac{1}{8}$ f-s.; signed E.G. 24.2.31.

562A Portland stone tablet in Jesus College, Cambridge, inscription in Latin, in memory of HENRY ARTHUR MORGAN.

Rubbing; $11\frac{3}{4}\times45$; endorsed 'E.G. Del. L.C. Sc. Portland stone, Jesus College, Cambridge, April, 1931'.

(See also No. 278.)

563 Plaque for house designed by Detmar Blow, Architect, inscribed: CHARLES WHIBLEY LIVED IN THIS HOUSE . . .

Rubbing of inscription; $13\frac{3}{4}\times29\frac{3}{4}$.

[This work was executed in 1931 by Prudence Pelham under E.G.'s guidance.]

564 Brass plate in memory of CHARLOTTE, Lady ROBERTSON C.B.E., d. 1931, wife of Sir Benjamin Robertson, K.C.S.I., K.C.M.G., C.I.E.

Pencil sketch; $\frac{1}{8}$ full-size; signed E.G. 1.6.31.

Drawing by George Friend (who cut the brass) with E.G.'s corrections, dated 1931.

Rubbing; $24\frac{1}{4}\times19\frac{1}{4}$; 1932.

565 Brass tablet, St. Nicholas, Brushford, Dulverton, Somerset, in memory of ELISABETH CATHARINE HOWARD, daughter of Henry and Charlotte Howard of Greystoke, wife of Henry, 4th Earl of Caernarvon. Born at Greystoke Castle, Penrith, 1856, died at Porto Fino, Italy, 1929.

Rubbing of inscription, which was designed by E.G. and engraved by George Friend; $23\times12\frac{1}{2}$; July 1931.

(See also No. 519.)

566 Hopton-Wood stone tablet for room in a house in Hampstead built by American and Scottish friends of JAMES RAMSAY MacDONALD, in gratitude for his visit to America as Prime Minister, in 1929.

Pencil drawing; $\frac{1}{4}$ f-s.; signed E.G. 28.7.31.

Rubbing; signed E.G. del. L.C. scp. Aug. 1931.

Size of tablet; $9\frac{1}{2}\times16\frac{3}{4}$.

567 Headstone about 4 ft. high, in memory of DUDLEY HENRY FORMAN, 1888–1930.

Pencil drawings (tinted); signed 'E.G. 3.8.31.

568 Portland gravestone, in Chichester Cemetery with inscriptions on both back and front.

(Front) In memory of HENRY HOLDING MOORE, 44 years Sacristan of Chichester Cathedral, 1839–1911, and of his wife JESSY MITCHELL MADDOCKS, 1844–1911.

(Back) In memory of their children, CECIL EDWARD, 1876–1895 & ARTHUR GORDON WENSKY, 1886–1912. Also of JESSY LILLIAN AND LILY & GILBERT DIXON.

Pencil drawing of front; 1 in. scale; signed E.G. 4.8.31. and of back; signed E.G. 5.8.31.

Rubbing of inscriptions on both sides; $44 \times 20\frac{3}{4}$; both signed E.G. del. L.C. sc., 1931.

[H. H. MOORE was Eric Gill's Father-in-Law.]

(See also No. 422.)

569 Portland headstone in Chiswick Cemetery in memory of GASPAR ROBERT KING, 1829–1910, and of his wife ROSE, 1833–1891 (Eric Gill's maternal grandparents). Also in memory of their daughter ELIZA-BETH, 1860–1926.

Pencil drawing; 1 in. scale; signed E.G. 4.8.31.

570 Portland headstone in memory of HENRY NICHOLAS MIDDLE-TON, 1845–1928 and his wife SOPHIA ELIZABETH 1848–1927.

Pencil drawing; $\frac{1}{6}$ f-s.; showing a Coat of Arms which is surmounted by a figure of Isaiah; signed E.G. 8.4.31.

Rubbing of inscription of one side of front of gravestone; $16\frac{1}{2} \times 16$; signed E.G. del., L.C.scp. September 1931.

571 Oak tablet, letters incised and gilded, in the Record Room, Oxford University Press: THIS ROOM FORMERLY THE OFFICE OF THE BIBLE PRINTERS OF THE UNIVERSITY, HAS BEEN FUR-NISHED AS THE RECORD ROOM OF THIS PRINTING HOUSE BY THE GIFT OF CONSTANCE MEADE GREAT GRAND-DAUGHTER OF BISHOP PERCY OF DROMORE, WHO IN HIS OWN DAY CONTRIBUTED TO THE LEARNING OF THIS PRESS.

Rubbing of tablet; $9\frac{1}{2} \times 52$; signed E.G. del., L.C. scp. September 1931.

572 Panel in entrance hall, Broadcasting House, London, recording: 1931 Architect, GEORGE VAL MYER; Partner, F. J. WATSON-HART;

Civil Engineer, M. T. TUDSBERY; Sculptor, ERIC GILL; Clerk of
Wks, G. R. BRITCHFORD; Master Bldr, W. HASSELDINE; Fore-
man, E. STAPLER.

Work executed October–November, 1931.

(See also inscription in bronze letters also in the entrance hall, No. 577.)

573 Recumbent gravestone of Portland stone in memory of EDITH
NETTLESHIP, 1871–1931.
Pencil drawing, tinted; scale 1 in.; signed E.G. 1.8.31.
Rubbing of inscription; 65½ × 27; signed E.G. del., L.C., scp., Oct, 1931.

574 Headstone of Cornish slate in St. Nun's, Pelynt, Looe, Cornwall, in
memory of WILLIAM SHUCKFORTH GRIGSON, Priest, 1845–1930.
Pencil drawing (tinted); signed E.G. 19.10.31. L. Cribb sc.

574A Inscription incised in stone for mantelpiece in *Elmstead*, West Wittering,
Sussex, the house then occupied by Sir Henry Royce. This read: QUIDVIS
RECTE FACTUM QUAMVIS HUMILE PRAECLARUM. It was
carved *c.* 1931.

How this came into being was recorded by Lieut.-Col. L. F. R. Fell, in an
article *Working for Royce* contributed to a special supplement of *The Guardian*,
March 27 1963, commemorating the centenary of Sir Henry Royce, born
March 27, 1863. We quote: ' . . . Gill was staying with his father, the Vicar
of West Wittering. Royce became friendly with Gill, and they often met. At
one of their meetings Gill asked Royce what he thought was the basic reason
for his success. Royce replied "I have always believed that whatever I do,
however humble the job is, if I do it as well as I can, it is noble." Gill was so
pleased with this thought that he had the words freely translated into Latin,
and presented Royce with the inscription carved over his fireplace.'

575 Portland tombstone surmounted by a crucifix and figures, together with
footstone showing the Madonna and Child, in Canford Cemetery, Bristol, in
memory of ABIGAIL PHILOMENA CHUTE, 1855–1931.
Pencil and wash drawings of both head and footstones; signed Eric Gill,
27.11.31.

576 Head and footstones of Portland stone in Canford Cemetery, Bristol, in
memory of DESMOND MACREADY CHUTE, 1895–1927.
Pencil drawing (tinted); signed E.G. 21.11.31.
Another drawing, on that which was done for Abigail Philomena Chute;
signed Eric Gill, 27.11.31.

577 Bronze letters on stone in entrance hall, Broadcasting House, Portland Place, London, W.1: DEO OMNIPOTENTI TEMPLVM HOC ARTIVM ET MVSARVM ANNO DOMINI MCMXXXI...
Architect's drawing; $1\frac{1}{2}$ in. scale; $6\frac{3}{4} \times 31\frac{1}{2}$; endorsed by E.G. 'tracing from drawing by E.G.'
There are separate tracings of the 4 in. bronze letters dated 23.12.31.
(See also No. 572.)

578 Portland headstone, with footstone, the latter with inscription in Hebrew characters, in Willesden Cemetery, in memory of ANNETTE LEWIS, 1862–1931, wife of Eliot Lewis.
Three pencil drawings; $\frac{1}{8}$ f-s.; all signed E.G. 15.12.31. & (2) 28.12.31.
Rubbing of inscription of headstone; $17\frac{1}{2} \times 12\frac{1}{2}$; beneath which is a rubbing of the Hebrew inscription $8\frac{1}{4}$ in. in length; signed E.G. del. L.C. scp. January 1932.

579 Hopton-Wood stone tablet now in the chapel at Pigotts, North Dean, High Wycombe (where Eric Gill lived), with inscription in Latin, surmounted by a dove: EMITTE SPIRITUM TUUM ET CREABUNTUR ET RENOVABIS FACIEM TERRAE.
Size of tablet; $20 \times 19\frac{1}{2}$.
Rubbing; endorsed 'E.G. del. & sc. March 1932 (for Venice Exhibition).'
The dove was carved by Michael Richey. This tablet was cut for an exhibition in Venice. A photograph of it appears as frontispiece to *Making and Thinking*, by Walter Shewring [London: Hollis & Carter, 1959].

580 Hopton-Wood stone tablet, inscription surmounted by Coat of Arms, in memory of SIR CHARLES HAMILTON RUSHOUT, Fourth and last Baronet, Late Royal Horse Guards, of Burford House, Tenbury, Wells. b. 1868 d. 1931. Buried at Longborough, Glos.
Pencil drawing; $\frac{1}{4}$ f-s.; signed E.G. 1.4.32.
Rubbing of inscription; $14\frac{1}{4} \times 35\frac{3}{4}$; signed E.G. del. L.C. scp. Sept. 1932.
Size of tablet; 42×38.

581 Head- and footstone, St. Lawrence, Besselsleigh, Abingdon, in memory of GERTRUDE MAY WALKER, d. 1930. Also of her husband the Revd. E. M. WALKER, D.D., Rector of the parish 1895–1920 and sometime Provost of Queen's College, Oxford.
On footstone, the initials: G.M.W.
Size of headstone; 54×28.
Pencil drawing; signed E.G. 5.8.1932.

582 Tablet of Hopton-Wood stone in memory of JULIA MARY
PLEISTER, NEE MILLER d. 1932.
Pencil drawing; signed E.G. 19.8.32.
Rubbing of tablet; 15 × 21¼; endorsed by E.G. 'L.C[ribb] del. et sc. The
first inscription done by L.C. for E.G. in wh. L.C. both drew & cut the
letters, Sept. 1932.'

583 Altar tomb in Ruislip Churchyard, Middlesex, about 6 ft. long, 2 ft. wide,
and 2 ft. 3 in. high, in memory of FAIRFAX HALL also of ANNIE
HALL, O.B.E., 1867–1932.
Pencil drawing; signed E.G. 20.8.32.

584 Hopton-Wood ledgerstone, All Saints Churchyard, Iden, Rye, Sussex, in
memory of ELIZABETH EMMA BEATRICE, BELOVED WIFE
OF ADMIRAL SIR AUBREY SMITH, K.B.E., C.B., M.V.O.,
1875–1931.
Scale drawing; ⅙ f-s. of 3 in. letters; signed E.G. 3.10.32.

584A Tablet of grey Hopton-Wood stone inscribed: IF THOU HAST A
LOAF OF BREAD SELL HALF AND BUY THE FLOWERS OF
THE NARCISSUS.
Rubbing; 11¼ × 30; endorsed (by E.G.) 'Donald Potter. Oct. 1932.'

585 Headstone in memory of ELEANOR MARY DERRICK, 1918–1932.
Daughter of Thomas and Margaret Derrick.
Pencil drawing; signed E.G. 9.12.32.
Another drawing is dated 30 Nov. 1934 to which is attached a note: 'Agreed
to this. E.G. 16.12.34.'
Headstone 30 in. square with 2 in. incised letters.

585A Alphabet with Roman capitals and lower-case letters and numerals
incised on Hopton-Wood stone, signed E.G. 1932. Commissioned by *Sculpture
& Memorials*, London.
This is reproduced in E.G.'s *Autobiography* facing p. 136.

586 Memorial in the central court of the Robert Thorner Charity Homes,
Regent's Park Road, Shirley, Southampton.
(a) Tablet recording the names of the Trustees in 1932.
Rubbing of inscription; 18¼ × 19½; undated and unsigned.
(b) Tablet giving details of the benefaction under the Will of ROBERT

THORNER, who died 17 July, 1690, and lies buried in Baddesley churchyard.
Rubbing of inscription; $48\frac{3}{4} \times 19\frac{1}{2}$; undated and unsigned.
Work executed c. 1932.

587 Portland ledgerstone in St. Marylebone Cemetery, London, N.W., in memory of ELINOR BEAUFOY MILTON, 1911–1931.
Pencil drawing; $\frac{1}{8}$ f-s.; signed E.G. 24.5.31. There are three later drawings all signed E.G., one dated 8.7.32 and the other two 19.10.32.
Rubbing of inscription; $20\frac{1}{2} \times 20\frac{1}{2}$; signed E.G., del., Donald P., scp., Jan., 1933.

588 Plaque of Portland stone in refectory of the House of the Resurrection, Mirfield, Yorks., in memory of CHARLES GORE, Bishop, 1853–1932.
Pencil sketch depicting Paschal Lamb; signed E.G. 20.1.33.
This plaque depicts the Paschal Lamb and carries the following inscription: SURREXI PRAE AMICITIA CAROLI GORE POSUIT ARCHI-TECTUS. It was the joint work of E.G. and Donald Potter.

589 Headstone in Golders Green cemetery, London, in memory of HENRY OPPENHEIMER, 1859–1932.
Pencil drawing; $1\frac{1}{2}$ in. scale; signed E.G. 23.9.32.
Rubbing of inscription; $19\frac{3}{4} \times 16\frac{1}{2}$; endorsed by E.G. 'L.C. for E.G. Feb. 1933.'

590 Portland head- and footstone at Cambridge in memory of IRENE ROBERTS, 1885–1932.
Pencil drawing; signed E.G. 21.3.33.

591 Grave-board at Suhr bei Aarau, Switzerland, in memory of MICHAEL D'OYLY CARTE. AGED 21 YEARS KILLED NEAR HERE IN AN ACCIDENT ON OCTOBER 23rd 1932. THE SON OF RUPERT AND DOROTHY D'OYLY CARTE OF LONDON.
Coloured perspective drawing; bears a note: 'Posts $5''$ square, length of letter-ing board about 6 feet.'; signed E.G. 28.3.33.

592 Hopton-Wood stone tablet in Eton College chapel in memory of HUGH MACNAGHTEN who lived in Jourdelay's Place, 1899–1920.
Pen and ink drawing; $\frac{1}{8}$ full-size; signed E.G. 19.4.33.
Rubbing; $22\frac{3}{4} \times 23\frac{3}{4}$.

593 Double headstone, of Portland stone, in memory of ALICE JAMESON, 1899–1932.
Pencil tracing; $\frac{1}{8}$ f-s.; portraying a nude female figure on either side of which are panels of incised letters; signed E.G. 10.4.32. This was duly carved but rejected by the cemetery authorities. At one time on loan to the Tate Gallery but was subsequently returned to Pigotts, High Wycombe.
A later drawing; $\frac{1}{12}$ f-s.; is also for a double headstone but this shows a crucifix above and between the two panels. This is signed E.G. 2.5.33.
The panel on the left bears incised letters: HOMO SICUT FOENVM . . . and on the right: ANTE FACIEM FRIGORIS . . .

594 Foundation stone for London University on the base of the tower, facing Malet Street, London, W.C., laid by King George V, 26th June, 1933.
Pencil drawing of $1\frac{1}{2}$ in. and 2 in. letters for portion of the inscription; signed E.G. 1.5.33.

595 Headstone of Hopton-Wood stone in Princes Risborough churchyard in memory of HARRY STALLWOOD, 1897–1933.
Pen and ink sketch by E.G., May 1933; endorsed 'job done by Anthony Foster. Oct 1933'.
Rubbing of inscription; 26 × 18; endorsed by E.G. 'H. W. Stone Anthony Foster del. & sc. Sept. 1933'.

596 Tablet of Roman stone on staircase in the premises of John Heal and Sons Limited, Tottenham Court Road, London, W.C., recording the Heads of the Business.
Pen and ink sketch; $\frac{1}{8}$ f-s., signed E.G. 6.7.33.
Rubbing; $50\frac{1}{2} \times 27\frac{1}{2}$; unsigned and undated.

597 Wooden tablet in memory of JAMES STEWART MONCREIFF PAUL, 1908–1932.
Pencil drawing; $\frac{1}{4}$ f-s.; signed E.G. 15.8.33.

598 Portland headstone at Nagpur, Madhya Pradesh, India, in memory of THOMAS VERNON SHUCKFORTH GRIGSON, infant son of W. V. Grigson, Deputy Commissioner of Nagpur, and Phyllis Grigson. Born Jan. 12, died July 21, 1932.
Pencil drawing; $\frac{1}{2}$ f-s.; signed E.G. 15.8.33; endorsed by E.G. 'Grigson $\frac{1}{2}$ full-size.'

Rubbing of inscription; $43 \times 13\frac{1}{2}$; endorsed by E.G. 'L.C. del. from E.G.'s $\frac{1}{2}$ f-s. drawing. L.C. sc. Jan. 1934.'

599 Gravestone of Portland stone in memory of BRIGDR-GEN. CHARLES PEARS FENDALL, C.B., C.M.G., D.S.O., 1861–1933. Pencil drawing; signed E.G. 1.10.33. and endorsed 'not done. E.G.'
Rubbing (of accepted design); $55\frac{1}{4} \times 28\frac{1}{2}$; signed E.G. & A.F. del., A.F. sc. Jan.–Feb. 1934.

600 York ledgerstone, St. Michael and All Angels, Himley, Dudley, Staffs., in memory of WILLIAM HUMBLE WARD, 2nd Earl of Dudley. Born 25th May 1867, died 29th June, 1932.
Rubbing; $41\frac{3}{4} \times 21$; signed L.C. del & sc., Nov. 1933.

601 Hopton-Wood stone tablet (inscription in Latin), in the War Memorial Chapel, Rossall School, Fleetwood, Lancs., in memory of HERBERT ARMITAGE JAMES, D.D. d. 1931.
Rubbing of inscription; $18\frac{1}{4} \times 28\frac{1}{2}$; signed E.G., del., L.C., sc., November, 1933.

602 Portland headstone at Little Hampden, Bucks., in memory of MARY BERNADETTE NUTTGENS, d. Feb., 1926.
Rubbing of inscription; $13\frac{1}{2} \times 9\frac{1}{2}$; signed Anthony Foster & E.G. del. A.F. sc. Nov., 1933.

603 Portland headstone at Speen, Bucks., in memory of EDITH T. E. HUELIN, 1857–1933.
Rubbing of inscription; 27×12; signed Anthony Foster & E.G. del. A.S. sc., December, 1933.

604 Headstone of York stone in the churchyard, St. James the Apostle, Bushey, Herts., in memory of WILLIAM HASLAM MILLS, Barrister-at-Law, 1874–1930.
Rubbing of inscription in 2 in. letters; $37\frac{1}{2} \times 17$; endorsed by E.G. 'L.C. del & sc. Dec., 1933'.

605 Hopton-Wood stone tablet in cloisters of New College, Oxford (the inscription in Latin), in memory of GILBERT CAROLI BOURNE, 1861–1933.
Pen and ink drawing; $\frac{1}{8}$ f-s.; signed E.G. 5.9.33.
Rubbing of tablet; $26\frac{1}{4} \times 34$; signed E.G. del. L.C. sc. Dec. 1933.
(See also No. 629.)

606 Recumbent gravestone in Wimbledon Cemetery in memory of DAVID BURNS, 1854–1932.

Pencil drawing; signed E.G. 20.8.33. and another (for the inscription); signed E.G. 7.12.33.

Half f-s. drawing for inscription; $38\frac{1}{2} \times 14$; signed E.G. 27.12.33.

607 Cross of Portland stone in the churchyard St. Wilfrid's, Burnsall, Skipton-in-Craven, Yorks., in memory of HENRY PHILIP DAWSON of Hartling-ton, 1850–1933, and of his wife MARY LOUISA, 1850–1932.

Pencil drawing; signed E.G. 27.1.34.

Drawing; half f-s., side view; signed E.G. 8.3.34.

Rubbing of inscription; $37 \times 20\frac{1}{2}$; endorsed 'Anthony Foster dr. & sc. April–May, 1934.'

608 The letters RADCLIFFE LIBRARY, approx. $3\frac{1}{2}$ in. high, on lintel over main door, together with three Coats of Arms, on the Radcliffe Science Library, South Parks Road, Oxford. 1934.

Length of inscription $76\frac{1}{4}$ in.

609 Garden seat of Portland stone in Victor Gollancz's garden at Brimpton, near Reading, in memory of HAROLD REDFERN GARDENER.

Pencil drawings; f-s. section and half f-s. elevation, also perspective sketch for seat, and pencil layout for side inscription, all on a single sheet; signed E.G. 27.12.33.

Rubbing of inscription (which is in Latin and Hebrew) on front panel: R. & V.G. HVNC HORTVLVM . . .; $12\frac{1}{2} \times 23\frac{1}{4}$, and on side: Harold Redfern, gardener; $1\frac{5}{8} \times 9\frac{3}{8}$.

Both rubbings on a single sheet; signed E.G. inv., L.C. sc. & del., Feb. 1934.

610 Memorial of Bethlehem stone in Jerusalem, in memory of KATRINA, First Lady Conway of Allington, Kent, d. 1933.

Rubbing of inscription; 26×25; signed E.G., Jerusalem, June 1934.

611 Headstone of Portland stone in Chester cemetery, depicting St. Francis in memory of FREDERICK COPLESTONE, C.B.E., J.P. of Chester. Also commemorated are FREDERICK LEWIS COPLESTONE, Lieut.-Commdr. R.N., d. November 1914, A. F. COPLESTONE-BOUGHEY, Commdr. R.N., d. May 1916, both of whom were killed on active service.

Preliminary sketch embodying figure of St. Francis; signed E.G. 29.1.34, also

H

pencil drawings of figure and inscription; $\frac{1}{12}$ f-s.; signed E.G. 30.1.34 together with one of the figure in outline dated 3.8.34.

Rubbing of inscription; $22\frac{1}{2} \times 23\frac{1}{4}$; signed E.G. del., L.C. sc. August, 1934.

612 Hopton-Wood stone tablet at Clocaenog, Ruthin, N. Wales, inscribed: LORD BAGOT'S PLANTATIONS WERE FELLED DURING AND AFTER THE GREAT WAR 1914–1918. THE FORESTRY COMMISSIONERS BEGAN TO PLANT CLOCAENOG FOREST IN 1930. 1933 R. L. ROBINSON, CHAIRMAN.

Pen and ink sketch; signed E.G. 7.12.33.

Rubbing; signed E.G. del. L.C. sc. Aug–Sept. 1934.

Actual size of tablet; $35\frac{1}{2} \times 47\frac{1}{2}$.

613 Portland headstone in churchyard of St. John the Evangelist, Tolpuddle, Dorset, in memory of JAMES HAMMETT TOLPUDDLE MARTYR PIONEER OF TRADES UNIONISM CHAMPION OF FREEDOM BORN 11 DECEMBER 1811 DIED 21 NOVEMBER 1891.

Pencil sketch; together with detail of moulding and panel signed E.G. 4.8.34

Rubbing of inscription; $31\frac{1}{4} \times 29$; signed E.G. & L.C. Aug. '34.

614 Hopton-Wood stone tablet on the coffin of DAVID PEPLER, 1906–1934, in the churchyard, St. Margaret's, Ditchling.

Rubbing; $23\frac{3}{4} \times 7\frac{3}{4}$; signed E.G. & L.C. sc. Sept. 3. 1934.

615 Hopton-Wood stone tablet at Sevenoaks, Kent: THIS ASSEMBLY HALL WAS GIVEN TO THE SCHOOL BY CHARLES PLUMPTRE JOHNSON CHAIRMAN OF THE GOVERNORS JUNE 1934.

Pen and ink sketch and pen and ink drawing; both signed E.G. and dated 27.5.34. and 11.8.34. respectively.

Rubbing of tablet; 9×18; signed E.G. del. L.C. sc. Sept. 1934.

616 Portland headstone in Canford Cemetery, Bristol, in memory of BERTRAM HUGHES RIDLER, 1865–1934.

Pencil sketch; signed E.G. 6.9.34.

617 Portland stone cross, St. Mary's cemetery, Kensal Green, London, in memory of ETHEL PES DI VILLA-MARINA, d. 14 October, 1933. The inscription surmounted by a crucifix in relief.

Pencil drawing; $\frac{1}{8}$ f-s. approx.; signed E.G. 10.9.34.

Rubbing of inscription; 14×11; endorsed 'L.C. for E.G. January 1935.'

618 Portland headstone, inscription surmounted by head and wings of a cherub, in memory of MARTIN JAMES, who died 24th Oct. 1933 aged 4.
Rough pencil sketch; ⅛ f-s.; signed E.G. 24.9.34.
Rubbing of inscription; 27 × 13½; signed A.F. for E.G. Oct. 1934.

619 Hopton-Wood headstone: MEMENTO/ MEI/ E.G./ LAPIDARII/ MCMXXXVI/ HEU MIHI.
Rubbing of inscription; 21¾ × 15½; signed E.G. del., D.P. scp. October 1934.
The carving was done for the Advertising Exhibition at Dorland Hall, London 1934, and by it E.G. anticipated his own death!
[This tombstone is referred to in a letter to Graham Carey published in *Letters of Eric Gill*, p. 409.]
(See also No. 762.)

620 Portland headstone: REMEMBER PHILOMEL. 1845–1923. ATE WORMS SANG SONGS R.I.P.
This was a sample carving done for the Advertising Exhibition, Dorland Hall, London, 1934.
Pencil sketch; unsigned and undated. On the reverse of this is an alternative inscription: PRAY FOR ME / PHILOMEL / Summer & Winter / as I lie with the / roof so near the / floor . . . / 1882–1936 / R.I.P.
Rubbing; 23¾ × 19; signed E.G. del., L.C. sc. October 1934.

621 Panel for Advertising Exhibition at DORLAND HALL December 1934 incorporating drawings of figures and various kinds of lettering and shorthand.
One-eighth full-size drawing (coloured); 13½ × 21¾; signed D.T. & E.G. inv. et del. Oct. 1934.

622 Headstone in cemetery adjoining the School Chapel, Douai Abbey, Upper Woolhampton, nr. Reading, in memory of OLIVIA FANNY WHITE, 1841–1933, Lady of the Manor of Bucklebury.
Pencil drawing; 1 in. scale; signed E.G. 30.11.34.

623 Portland headstone in memory of OLIVE BEATRICE BOCQUET, 1884–1932.
Pencil sketch for top of stone; signed E.G. 30.12.34.
Rubbing of inscription; 12 × 26; signed E.G. del. L.C. sc., Dec. 1934.

624 Hopton-Wood stone headstone in memory of HENRY COTTERILL TILLARD, M.A. (Oxon), 1859–1934, of Cargilfield School.

Size of headstone: $40\frac{1}{4} \times 27$; pencil sketch, in perspective; signed 'E.G.' but undated.
Work executed c. Dec. 1934.

625 Brass plate set within a Hopton-Wood stone frame, St. Peter and St. Paul, Great Missenden, Bucks., in memory of ERNEST ROBERT LINDLEY, 1860–1935.
Drawing of portion of frame, in section; (undated) c. 1935.
(Cf. No. 648.)

626 Raised ledgerstone of Portland stone, St. Lawrence, Bourton-on-the-Hill, Glos., in memory of DIXON HENRY DAVIES, 1859–1934.
Pencil drawing; signed E.G. 4.10.34.
Rubbing of inscriptions which run around the edges of the ledgerstone, measuring $28\frac{1}{4}$ in. at each end and $71\frac{1}{4}$ in. on each side; signed E.G. del. Thos. J. Gill Sc. (Bourton-on-the-Hill) 1935.

627 Hopton-Wood stone tablet (the inscription in Latin, in $\frac{3}{4}$ in. caps.) on S. wall of S. transept, Merton College, Oxford, in memory of WALTER WYBERGH HOW, d. 1932.
F-s. drawing; signed Eric G. 21.12.34.
Size of tablet; $15\frac{1}{4} \times 25\frac{1}{4}$.
Rubbing; signed E.G. del., L.C. scp. Jan. 1935.

628 Portland headstone in memory of HENRY ALBERT SAUL, F.R.I.B.A., 1869–1933.
Pencil drawing; approx. $\frac{1}{8}$ f-s.; signed E.G. 21.12.34.
Rubbing of inscription; $17 \times 15\frac{1}{4}$; signed L.C. for E.G. Jan. 1935.

629 Gravestone in the churchyard St. Andrew, Sandford-on-Thames, in memory of GILBERT CHARLES BOURNE, D.Sc., F.R.S., 1861–1933.
Pencil drawing for portion of inscription; $4\frac{3}{4} \times 22$; signed E.G. 22.1.35.
(See also No. 605.)
[An inscription, in memory of Constance M. G. Bourne, 1864–1954, was added later by another hand.]

630 Mural tablet of Green Hornton stone in the cloisters, New College, Oxford, in memory of JOHN GALSWORTHY, O.M., 1867–1933.
Pencil drawing; $\frac{1}{4}$ f-s.; signed E.G. 20.2.35.
Actual size of tablet; $11 \times 23\frac{1}{2}$; rubbing signed E.G. & L.C. April, 1935.

631 Foundation stone of Portland stone for the Guildhall, Kingston-on-Thames, and another stone commemorating the opening of the Hall by H.R.H. Princess Alice, Countess of Athlone, 3rd July, 1935.
Rubbing of specimen of lettering for foundation stone (letters 2 in. high); signed E.G. del. L.C. sc. 1935.

632 Recumbent gravestone of Portland stone, All Saints', Sutton, Beds., with the lower part of the inscription in Hebrew, in memory of GEORGE HERBERT BOX, Priest, M.A., D.D., 1869–1933.
Pencil drawing; $\frac{1}{8}$ f-s.; signed E.G. 20.2.35. This is accompanied by two layouts for the Hebrew text.
Rubbing; signed E.G. inv. et del., L.C. sc. March 1935.
Actual size of gravestone; 74 × 38.

633 Lettering 'BENTALLS' for fascia, with neon lights, for Bentall's Department Store, Kingston-on-Thames, Surrey.
Drawing of $4\frac{3}{4}$ in. letters; signed E.G. 20.3.35.

634 Head and kerb stones of Portland stone in Putney Vale cemetery London, in memory of WILLIAM ORPEN, 1878–1931.
Pencil drawing; signed E.G. 13.5.35.
Rubbing of inscription; $18\frac{1}{2} \times 16\frac{1}{2}$; signed E.G. del., L.C. sc. August 1935.

635 Recumbent gravestone of Delabole slate in St. John's churchyard, Hampstead, in memory of A. R. ORAGE, 1878–1934.
Drawing in perspective; signed E.G. 13.5.35.
Rubbing of inscription; $75\frac{1}{4} \times 28\frac{1}{4}$; signed E.G. del. L.C. sc. 7.9.35. [*See Plate XV*]

636 Monolith of Portland stone, 12 ft. high, at foot of Headington Hill, Oxford, inscribed: THIS PARK WAS ACQUIRED BY THE OXFORD PRESERVATION TRUST THROUGH THE LIBERALITY OF THE PILGRIM TRUST AND DAVID AND JOANNA RANDALL-MacIVER. 1932.
Pencil sketch and drawings; signed E.G. 14.5.35. and 17.5.35.
The finished drawing is in the John Johnson Collection at the University Press, Oxford.

637 Headstone of Portland stone, the inscription surmounted by Coat of Arms, in Manor Park Cemetery, Essex, in memory of ERNEST JOHN WIGNALL, 1875–1933, Registrar of East London College for forty years.
Pencil drawing (in perspective); signed E.G. 14.6.35.

Rubbing of inscription and shield; $25\frac{1}{2} \times 28$; signed E.G. inv. L.C., del & sc., Aug. '35.

638 Portland ledger graveslab in memory of HUGH WESTERN, 1876–1934, younger son of Lieut.-Col. James Halifax Western, C.M.G., R.E., and husband of Mary Theodora Western.
Pencil drawing; signed E.G. 7.6.35.
Rubbing of inscription; $53 \times 28\frac{1}{4}$; signed E.G. inv. L.C. del & sc., July, 1935.

639 Recumbent gravestone, St. John the Evangelist, Coatbridge, Lanark, in memory of ANDREW KIRKWOOD McCOSH, 1841–1916, of Merksworth & Parkhill Dairy, Ayrshire.
Pencil drawing, in perspective; signed E.G. 23.7.35.
Rubbing of inscription; $16\frac{3}{4} \times 38\frac{1}{2}$; signed E.G. del. and sc. Jan. 1936.
Dimensions of stone; 81×45.

639A Tablet of York stone, St. John the Evangelist, Coatbridge, Lanark, in memory of JAMES McCOSH, 1872–1903, SARA MACANDREW McCOSH, 1874–1877 and MARY SARA McCOSH, 1882–1883.
Pencil drawing; $\frac{1}{8}$ f-s.; signed E.G. 3.9.35.
Size of tablet; 24×27.
Rubbing; $23\frac{1}{2} \times 26$; signed E.G. inv., L.C. del. et sc. Jan. '36.

639B Gravestone of York stone, St. John the Evangelist, Coatbridge, Lanark, in memory of WILLIAM WADDELL McCOSH, 1883–1935.
Unfinished pencil drawing; signed E.G. 18.11.35.
Rubbing of inscription; $9\frac{1}{2} \times 35\frac{1}{2}$; signed E.G. del. and sc. Jan. 1936.

640 Head and footstones of Portland stone in memory of OLIVER PRIOR, 1878–1934, Fellow of St. John's College, Cambridge, and first Drapers Professor of French.
Pencil drawing (coloured); endorsed 'Approved'; signed E.G. 28.4.35.
Rubbing of inscription on headstone; $37 \times 25\frac{1}{2}$.
Rubbing of inscription on footstone; $8\frac{1}{2} \times 6\frac{1}{2}$.
Both rubbings signed E.G. inv. L.C. del & sc. July–August 1935.

641 Headstone of Hopton-Wood stone in Golders Green cemetery, London, in memory of NELLIE daughter of Henry and Clara OPPENHEIMER.
Pencil sketch; $\frac{1}{4}$ f-s.; signed E.G. 15.8.35.
Rubbing of portion of inscription; $21\frac{1}{2} \times 16\frac{1}{2}$; signed E.G. del. L.C. sc. November, 1935.

642 Headstone of Hopton-Wood stone with inscription in Pitman's shorthand which being interpreted reads: IN MEMORY OF JOHN SMITH. 1870–1935.

The 'commemoration' is hypothetical as the piece was cut merely for an exhibition of the Arts & Crafts Exhibition Society, in 1936. It was also shown in the French Gallery, November 1936.

Pencil sketch; $5\frac{3}{4} \times 3\frac{3}{4}$; signed E.G. Oct. '35 for A & C. Exhbtn.

Rubbing; $23\frac{3}{4} \times 14\frac{1}{2}$; signed E.G. inv. E.G. & D.K. del. & sc. Oct. 1935. (See also No. 655A.)

643 Hopton-Wood stone tablet in St. James-the-Less, Hadleigh, Essex, in memory of FRANCIS EDWARD CARTER, Rector of Hadleigh and Dean of Bocking, 1911–27, d. 1935.

Pen and ink sketch from E.G.'s hand but neither dated nor signed.

Rubbing of inscription; $11\frac{1}{4} \times 35\frac{3}{4}$; signed E.G. del., L.C.scp., December 1935.

644 Tablet of Hopton-Wood stone; ELMSTEAD; for house in West Wittering, Chichester.

Pencil drawing, full-size; endorsed '(for Hugh Deut) E.G. del. A.F. sc. Dec. '35'.

Rubbing of tablet; $5\frac{1}{2} \times 20\frac{1}{2}$; signed E.G. del., A.F. sc. December, 1935.

644A A portrait panel ($15 \times 20\frac{1}{2}$) in Cambridge of Lord Rutherford, inscribed RUTHERFORD.

The drawing for this is endorsed by E.G. 'from portrait made 13.12.32'.

Rubbing; $20 \times 15\frac{1}{2}$; endorsed by E.G. 'Rutherford 9.12.35' and 'A.F. cut the letters 19.12.35'.

645 Portland headstone in memory of MARGUERITE MAY HUGGETT, 1897–1934.

Pencil drawings; signed E.G. 11.12.35 and E.G. 12.12.35.

Rubbing; $30\frac{1}{2} \times 23\frac{1}{2}$; signed E.G. inv., L.C., del. scp., February, 1936.

645A Inscription, letters incised and coloured in red, on statue of the Immaculate Conception in Ratcliffe College, Leicester: MARIA SINE LABE ORIGINALI CONCEPTA O P N. The statue is approximately 4 ft. high.

In his diary 24 January 1936 E.G. records having drawn this inscription. (See also No. 645B.)

645B Inscription, letters incised and coloured in red, on the pedestal of a statue representing the Sacred Heart, in Ratcliffe College, Leicester: MISEREBITUR SECUNDUM MULTITUDINEM MISERATIONUM SUARUM. The statue is approximately 4 ft. high.
In his diary 24 January 1936 E.G. records having drawn this inscription.
(See also No. 645A.)

646 Hopton-Wood stone tablet inscribed: IN HOC COGNOVIMVS CHARITATEM DEI QVONIAM ILLE ANIMAM SVAM . . .
Rubbing of inscription; $25\frac{1}{2} \times 37$; signed E.G. inv., E.G. & D.K. del. D.K. sc., 1936.
[This was exhibited at the French Gallery, November 1936. Exhibit No. 32.]

647 Cross and kerbing of Green Hornton stone in Putney Vale Cemetery, in memory of DORIS ELISABETH ANSTED, 1878–1935.
Pencil drawing (coloured) of cross and kerbing; signed E.G. 11.12.35 and another signed E.G. 22.2.36.
Rubbing of inscription; $27 \times 12\frac{3}{4}$; signed E.G. del., L.C. scp. Ap.1936.

648 Portland headstone with kerbing, Holy Trinity Church, Northwood, Middx., in memory of ERNEST ROBERT LINDLEY, 1860–1935, and of his wife ADELAIDE, 1858–1935.
Pencil drawing (coloured) of headstone and kerbs; signed E.G. 24.2.36.
Rubbing of inscription; $31\frac{1}{2} \times 25$; signed E.G. & L.C. del. L.C. scp. April 1936.
(See also No. 625.)

649 Headstone in memory of ALBERT STEPHEN O'BRIEN, d. 28 February, 1936.
Pen and ink sketch by E.G., unsigned and undated.

650 Hopton-Wood stone panel in the MARGARET MACMILLAN House at Wrotham, Sevenoaks, Kent; built by the generosity of Lettice Floyd and opened by the Duchess of York.
Pen and ink sketch; unsigned and undated, but in E.G.'s hand.
Rubbing of panel; $15\frac{1}{2} \times 37\frac{1}{2}$; signed E.G. inv. L.C. del. et scp., March 1936.

651 Inscription, surmounted by five Coats of Arms (coloured), incised direct on South-west pier, St. Mary's, Hackney Wick, London (Eton College Mission), in memory of WILLIAM CARTER, sometime Bishop of Zululand, Bishop of Pretoria and Archbishop of Capetown.
Coloured drawing; signed E.G. 17.4.36.

652 Inscription, surmounted by four Coats of Arms (coloured), incised direct on North-west pier, St. Mary's, Hackney Wick, London (Eton College Mission), in memory of ST. CLAIR DONALDSON, sometime Archbishop of Brisbane and Bishop of Salisbury.
Coloured drawing; signed E.G. 17.4.36.

653 Head and footstones of Portland stone in memory of LESLIE GEORGE WYLDE, 1894–1935.
The letters A N Z Y incised on the footstone.
Pencil drawing (coloured); signed E.G. 28.3.36.
Rubbing of inscription on headstone; $24 \times 26\frac{3}{4}$; signed E.G. inv. L.C. del. & sc., May 1936.

654 Headstone in memory of ANNIE ELIZABETH MAYNARD 1865–1935.
Pencil drawing; signed E.G. 9.5.36.
Rubbing of inscription; 21×18.

655 Portland ledgerstone, the inscription in Latin, in Wimbledon Cemetery, in memory of CLARA SWINBURNE BURNS, 1866–1935.
Rubbing of inscription; $73\frac{1}{2} \times 30$; signed E.G. & L.C. del., L.C. scp. May 1936.

655A Headstone of Hopton-Wood stone with inscription in Gregg's shorthand which being interpreted reads: IN THE BEGINNING WAS THE WORD.
Rubbing; $23\frac{3}{4} \times 14\frac{1}{2}$; signed E.G. inv. E.G. & D.K. del. & sc. June 1936.
[This was cut for exhibition purposes and was shown at the French Gallery, November 1936.]
(See also No. 642.)

656 Recumbent gravestone of Portland stone in memory of JOHN CHRISTOPHER WOOD, PAINTER, 1901–1930.
Pencil drawings (in perspective) of two alternative designs; signed E.G. 28.3.36 and 28.4.36.
Length of gravestone 74 in.
Rubbing of inscription; $15\frac{1}{2} \times 23\frac{3}{4}$; signed E.G. del. L.C., scp., June, 1936.

657 Portrait tablet of Portland stone set in a surround of Clipsham stone, in memory of Baron ANATOLE VON HUGEL, 1883–1922, for Cambridge Museum of Archaeology, of which he was Curator.

Pencil sketch (tinted); 1 in. scale; signed E.G. 24.6.36.; and f-s. detail of moulding for the portrait; signed E.G. 28.7.36.

658 Portland stone tablet in St. Paul's Cathedral, London, in memory of Admiral of the Fleet CHARLES EDWARD MADDEN, 1st Bt. of Kells, Co. Kilkenny, G.C.B., O.M., G.C.V.O., K.C.M.G., D.C.L.Oxon, Ll.D., 1862–1935.
Coloured sketch; $\frac{1}{12}$ f-s.; on which a crest has been superimposed; signed E.G. 25.6.36.
(See also No. 692.)

659 Inscription on Hopton-Wood stone: ET ALIAS OVES . . .
Designed and drawn by E.G. cut by David Kindersley, c. February 1936.
[This was exhibited at the French Gallery, November 1936. Exhibit No. 33.]

660 Bas-relief stone triptych *The Re-creation of Man* in the Council Lobby of the Peace Palace, League of Nations, Geneva.
The central panel (28 ft. long and 7 ft. high) depicts the naked figure of a man with inscription: QUID EST HOMO MEMOR ES EJUS? AD IMAGINEM DEI CREAVIT ILLUM. This is followed by the opening lines of poem by Gerald Manley Hopkins, *The Wreck of the Deutschland*: 'THOU MASTERING ME . . .'
This work, executed between 1937–38 (though drawings were submitted in August 1935), was the gift of the Government of the United Kingdom.

661 Head and footstones at St. Mary the Virgin, Buckland, Betchworth, Surrey, in memory of MARY BEVAN.
Pencil drawing; $\frac{1}{2}$ f-s.; showing carving of cherub and first line of the inscription in $1\frac{1}{2}$ in. letters; signed E.G. 7.8.36.

662 Tablet of Hopton-Wood stone on the wall of the Monastery, Capel-y-ffin, near Abergavenny, Mon.: REMEMBER CHARLIE STONES FAITHFUL FRIEND & GUARDIAN OF THIS HOUSE 1928–1935.
Rubbing of tablet; $12\frac{1}{2} \times 19\frac{1}{2}$; signed E.G. del J.C. sc. May, 1937.
Work executed August 1936.
(See also No. 680.)

663 Portland headstone in memory of HELEN BOWER 1854–1936.
Pen and ink sketch; signed E.G. Sept. 1936, and endorsed 'Capt. Jameson'.

664 Stone tablet commemorating the installation of electric lighting in the Chancel of . . . Church in memory of GEORGE RUDDLE, d. 1923 and his wife, NORA CAROLINE, d. 1923.
Pen and ink drawing; signed E.G. 29.9.36.
Size of tablet approx. 8 × 12.

665 Hopton-Wood stone tablet, recording names of vicars of St. Andrew's, Monk Wearmouth, Sunderland, erected in 1936, in memory of the Rev. WALTER JOHNSON, 4th Vicar, 1929–1935.
Half f-s. drawing; 22 × 13½; signed E.G. 31.7.36.
Rubbing of inscription; 11¼ × 23¼; signed E.G. inv. L.C. sc. November 1936.

666 Head and ledgerstone of Portland stone in Putney Vale cemetery, in memory of HAZEL LAVERY, 1886–1935.
Rubbing of headstone; 22 × 23¾; signed E.G. inv., L.C. del & sc. December, 1936.

667 Raised ledgerstone in memory of HORATIO NELSON RITCHIE, 1882–1936, A BELOVED PHYSICIAN.
Pencil sketch by E.G.; but undated and unsigned; c. 1936.

668 An Alphabet of Roman and lower-case letters and numerals, designed by Eric Gill, carved on Hopton-Wood stone by Laurie Cribb.
Rubbing; 28 × 24½; endorsed by E.G. 'E.G. del L.C. sc. July 1935 (for Sculptured Mems. & Headstones Company)'.

669 Panel of Green Hornton stone in Witney, Oxon., in memory of D. J. SMITH.
Rubbing of some of the letters; signed L.C. del. et sc. March 1936.

670 Portland stone headstone in memory of MARION LILIAS HAMILTON-RUSSELL, 1876–1934, wife of Arthur Hamilton-Russell of Neatham Manor, Alton.
Drawings; (a) In pencil (coloured); signed E.G. 9.7.36. (b) In pen and ink, in perspective; signed E.G. 19.1.37.
Rubbing of inscription; 33 × 28; signed E.G.inv., L.C.dr. & sc. Feb.–Mch. 1937.

671 Monument, with inscription on Delabole slate, intended for the grave of THOMAS BARNES 1785–1841, in Kensal Green Cemetery, London.

Panels also commemorate SARAH DUNN, d. 1838 & MARY BARNES, d. 1852.

Pen and ink sketch; $\frac{1}{8}$ f-s., and layout, letters of full size; both signed E.G. 6.2.37. Another layout, letters of full size; signed E.G. 7.2.37.

Rubbings; the inscriptions for THOMAS BARNES; $18\frac{3}{4} \times 52\frac{1}{2}$ & $17\frac{1}{2} \times 52\frac{1}{2}$. The SARAH DUNN inscription; $19\frac{1}{2} \times 13\frac{1}{4}$.

The MARY BARNES inscription; $15\frac{1}{2} \times 12\frac{3}{4}$.

All rubbings; signed E.G. del L.C. sc. Oct.–Nov. 1937.

[This work, though executed, was not erected. It is now in the hands of the Times Publishing Co.]

(See also No. 734A.)

672 Plaques of de Freyne's French limestone, for beds in . . . hospital, endowed by the Prudential Assurance Co.

(a) 'THE SARAH LEWIS BED, 1932.'

Rubbing of inscription; $6 \times 19\frac{1}{2}$.

(b) 'THE WESTON BED, 1936.'

Rubbing of inscription; $11\frac{1}{2} \times 19\frac{1}{2}$.

(c) 'THE PRUDENTIAL ASSURANCE Co. Ltd. BED, 1930'.

Rubbing of inscription; 6×16.

All rubbings; signed E.G., inv., L.C. del. et. sc. February, 1937.

[Inquiries of the Assurance Company have failed to produce any information as to the whereabouts of this hospital.]

673 Sundial of Blue Hornton stone with semi-recumbent figure of a woman (carved by Anthony Foster) surmounted by an inscription (carved by E.G.): WHEN THE SUN IS NOT SHINING I DO THIS FOR FUN.

Pencil drawing and sketch, the latter endorsed by E.G. 'March, 1937'.

[This was carved for exhibition purposes and sold to a customer in the U.S.A.]

674 Portland stone tablet in the Parish Church of St. Andrew, Farnham, Surrey, inscribed: TO THE MEMORY OF GEORGE STURT OF THIS TOWN. HE WROTE WITH UNDERSTANDING AND DISTINCTION OF THE WHEELWRIGHTS' CRAFT AND ENGLISH PEASANT LIFE. BORN 1863—DIED 1927.

[This tablet was unveiled by Arundel Esdaile in November 1937.]

675 Gravestone with a Crucifix and figure of Our Lady, at Beaconsfield, Bucks., in memory of GILBERT KEITH CHESTERTON, 1874–1936 and of FRANCES, his wife, 1869–1938.

[The original work was carried out in 1937 and the additional inscription, in memory of Frances Chesterton, in January 1939.]

676 Portland headstone in Surbiton Cemetery in memory of MARIAN MOODY.
Designed by E.G. March 1937, the carving by Anthony Foster and inscription cut by Laurence Cribb, 1937. An additional inscription was cut in 1939.

677 Wall tablet, with portrait in relief, in the Maharani Hospital, Jagdalpur, Bastar State, Madhy Pradesh, India, in memory of MAHARANI PRAFULLA KUMARI DEVI, 1910–1936.
Pencil drawing for portrait and inscription; signed E.G. 16.3.37.
[This is now in the possession of Mr. E. S. Hyde, Heswall, Cheshire, who commissioned the work.]

678 Tablet of Hopton-Wood stone at Holkham, inscription surmounted by Coat of Arms, in memory of ALICE EMILY WHITE, wife of Thomas William Coke, 3rd Earl of Leicester, 1855–1936.
Pencil drawing (coloured); unsigned but endorsed in E.G.'s handwriting 'Lady Leicester, Holkham'.
Actual size, approx.; $29\frac{1}{2} \times 41\frac{1}{2}$.
Work executed 1937.

679 Portland headstone in churchyard of St. Mary & St. Bartholomew, Cranborne, Dorset, in memory of MICHAEL CHARLES JAMES CECIL. 1918–34.
Pen and ink sketch; signed E.G. 6.1.37. and two rough pencil sketches for wings, one of which is signed E.G. 27.2.37.
Two pencil drawings; both signed E.G. 23.1.37.
F-s. pencil drawing of one wing and a cross; signed E.G. 22.2.37.
Rubbing of inscription; $16\frac{1}{2} \times 22\frac{1}{2}$; endorsed 'E.G. inv. L.C. del. & sc. (J.S. sclptd. Angels' wings) April 1927'.

680 Portland headstone in the graveyard of the church at Capel-y-ffin, Abergavenny, Mon.: REMEMBER CHARLIE STONES CARPENTER DIED 1935 R.I.P.
Pencil sketch; signed E.G. Ap. 1937.
Rubbing of headstone; $22 \times 12\frac{1}{2}$; signed E.G. del. J.C. sc. May, 1937.
(See also No. 662.)

681 Ledgerstone of Portland stone, St. Barnabas, Burnmoor, County Durham, in memory of Major-General the Hon. Sir WILLIAM LAMBTON, K.C.B., C.M.G., D.S.O., 1863–1936.
Pencil drawing (tinted); signed E.G. 11.1.37.
Rubbing of inscription; 63¾ × 24½; signed E.G. inv. A.F. del & sc. May 1937.

682 Hopton-Wood stone tablet on West wall in Holy Rood Church, Watford, in memory of JOSEPH PATRICK KEATING, 1862–1924. Rector of the parish for 22 years.
Pen and ink drawing; ⅛ f-s.; signed E.G. 13.3.37.
Rubbing of inscription; 17¼ × 33½; signed E.G. inv. A.F. del. & sc. May 1937.

683 Headstone of Portland stone in Hastings cemetery, in memory of ROBERT ARTHUR COOMBS, Priest, 1869–1924, and of his wife BERTHA GEORGINA, 1869–1926.
Pen and ink sketch; signed E.G. 9.3.37.
Actual size, approx. 42 × 24.

684 Tablet in the Eye Hospital (Hospital of St. John) Jerusalem, in memory of GENEVIEVE LADY WATSON, d. 31 Dec. 1936, Dame of Grace of the Order of St. John of Jerusalem, widow of Sir Charles Watson, R.E., K.C.M.G.
Pencil sketch; endorsed '(Jerusalem Eye Hospital)' and signed E.G. 2.6.37.
Size of tablet approx. 34 × 45.

685 Memorial tablet in Scotch Church, Jerusalem, in memory of the men of the BLACK WATCH, ROYAL HIGHLANDERS who fell in battle in Palestine, 1917–1918.
Pencil sketch showing regimental crest; signed E.G. 18.6.37.
This tablet was commissioned in 1937 by the 1st and 2nd Battalions the Black Watch, Sir Arthur Wauchope, General.

686 Tablet in the Eye Hospital, Jerusalem, commemorating the life and work of WILLIAM EDMUND CANT, M.B.E., M.D., F.R.C.S., d. 1936.
Pencil sketch; unsigned but endorsed by E.G. 'Jerusalem Eye Hospital June 1937'.

687 Portland headstone in Wolvercote Cemetery, Oxford, in memory of ELEANOR CONSTANCE LODGE, D. Litt., C.B.E. 1869–1936., sometime Vice-Principal of Lady Margaret Hall and Principal of Westfield College, University of London.

Pencil drawing; $\frac{1}{12}$ f-s.; signed E.G. 12.1.37.

Rubbing of inscription; $34\frac{3}{4} \times 32$; signed E.G. inv., L.C. del. et scp., June 1937.

688 Painted lettering for bookshop of John and Edward Bumpus, Ltd., Oxford Street, London, W.: THERE ARE, IT MAY BE, SO MANY KINDS OF VOICES IN THE WORLD, AND NONE OF THEM IS WITHOUT SIGNIFICANCE (1 Corinthians, 14–10).

Painted by Denis Tegetmeier, 1937.

[When the bookshop was vacated, these boards were acquired by The Monotype Corporation.]

689 Portland stone tablet in the Dockyard Church, Portsmouth, in memory of Sir JOHN DONALD KELLY, 1871–1936, Admiral of the Fleet, G.C.B., G.C.V.O.

Pen and ink drawing; $\frac{1}{8}$ full-size; signed E.G. 4.3.37.

Rubbing of tablet; $47\frac{1}{2} \times 25\frac{1}{4}$; signed E.G. inv. L.C. del. & sc. July 1937.

(See also No. 693.)

689A Delabole slate tablet St. Peter, Greenham, Wellington, Somerset, recording a benefaction given by Mary Kelly the widow of ADMIRAL SIR JOHN KELLY, July 1937.

Rubbing; $10 \times 12\frac{3}{4}$; signed E.G. del. L.C., sc. Oct. 1937.

(See also No. 693.)

690 Slate panel over main entrance of Blackfriars, St. Giles, Oxford, inscribed: HUNC CONVENTUM ALTERUM NOVUM EADEM . . .

Pen and ink drawing; $\frac{1}{8}$ f-s.; signed E.G. 30. Ap. 37.

Rubbing of panel; $12\frac{1}{4} \times 35\frac{1}{4}$; signed E.G. del., A.F[oster]. scp. July '37.

691 Head and footstones in churchyard at St. Thomas, Chevithorne, Tiverton, Devon, in memory of MICHAEL LUDOVIC HEATHCOAT AMORY, 1914–1936.

Pen and ink drawing for both stones dated 1936 also a pencil drawing (coloured) of footstone: 'M.L.H.A.' and of a fish signed E.G. 19.9.37.

Another drawing of Coat of Arms; signed E.G. 31.7.37.

692 Recumbent gravestone of Portland stone, in Chichester Cemetery, in memory of JOHN WILLIAM MADDEN, 1825–1875, Captain Adjutant Royal Sussex Light Infantry and of his son CHARLES EDWARD MADDEN, Admiral of the Fleet, 1862–1935. First Baronet of Kells, Co. Kilkenny.

Pencil drawing (in perspective); signed E.G. 5.8.37.
Actual size, approx. 78 × 36.
(See also No. 658.)

692A Table-stone paperweight with inscription: WHATSOEVER THY HAND FINDETH TO DO DO IT WITH THY MIGHT.
Actual size 4½ × 2½.
This was cut for Wilma Lady Cawdor in August 1937.

692B Table-stone (slate) paperweight with inscription: I AM AN AMBASS-ADOR IN BONDS THAT THEREIN I MAY SPEAK BOLDLY AS I OUGHT TO SPEAK
Actual size 4⅜ × 2⅜.
Rubbing; endorsed 'Slate—E.G. 12.8.37'.
This was cut for Wilma Lady Cawdor as a gift to the late Charles Morgan.

693 Tablet of Portland stone, St. Peter, Greenham, Wellington, Somerset, in memory of Sir JOHN DONALD KELLY, 1871–1936, Admiral of the Fleet, G.C.B., G.C.V.O.
Rubbing of inscription; 42¼ × 25¼; signed E.G. inv. L.C. del. et sc., April 1937.
A later inscription commemorates MARY his wife, 1880–1937.
Rubbing of inscription; 9¼ × 23¼; signed L.C. del., scp. March–April 1938.
(See also No. 689.)

694 Inscriptions on stones, UNIVERSITY PRESS, on either side of front entrance to the Pitt Building, The University Press, Cambridge.
E.G. del., Anthony Foster scp. 1937.

695 Delabole slate tablet with Hopton-Wood surround in University College, Oxford, in memory of ANDRE JOHN MESNARD MELLY, A.M., M.C., M.A., B.M., Commni. of the college, 1919–1922. Leader of the British Red Cross Unit in Abyssinia, who died at Addis Ababa, May 5, 1936, aged 37.
Pen and ink sketch; ⅛ full-size; signed E.G. 10.4.37.
Rubbing; 13 × 20; signed E.G., del., L.C. sc. September 1937.

696 Delabole slate tablet in the laboratory of the Marie Curie Hospital, Hampstead, recording the equipment of the laboratory in memory of HELEN CHAMBERS, 1879–1935.
Rubbing; 11 × 23¾; signed E.G. del., L.C. sc. September 1937.

697 Head and kerb stones of red Mansfield stone in memory of EDMUND COMMELINE LLOYD, 1888–1936, of Pitsworthy.
Pencil drawing, in perspective; signed E.G. 21.9.37.
Actual size 24 × 30.

698 Portland headstone in Brent Knoll Churchyard, Somerset, in memory of FREDERICK JOSEPH WALMSEY HUNTER, 1876–1936.
Pencil sketch; $\frac{1}{8}$ f-s.; signed E.G. 23.9.37.

699 Portland headstone in the churchyard of All Saints, Castle Cary, Bath, in memory of HENRY HOBHOUSE, 1854–1937.
Work executed 1937.

700 Headstone of Portland stone in memory of GILLIAN MEROWE CORYTON, 1928–1935.
Rubbing of inscription; $20\frac{1}{2} \times 12\frac{1}{2}$; endorsed in E.G.'s handwriting 'John Sharpe Scp. Oct. 1937'.

701 Portland stone gravestone in memory of FRANKLIN JOHN KING, 1855–1936.
Rubbing of inscription; $20\frac{1}{2} \times 12$; endorsed in E.G.'s handwriting 'John Sharpe. scp. October 1937'.

702 Headstone in the churchyard of St. Mary the Virgin, Langley-Marish, Slough, in memory of WILLIAM FRANCIS NASH, 1931–1935.
Pencil sketch; unsigned but in E.G.'s hand; Dec., 1937.
Actual size approx. $39\frac{1}{2} \times 20$.

703 Delabole slate tablet in memory of FREDERICK HAMLYN, 1845–1904.
Rubbing; $13 \times 21\frac{3}{4}$; signed E.G. del. L.C. scp. December, 1937.

704 Delabole slate tablet in memory of CHRISTINE HAMLYN, 1856–1936, wife of Frederick Hamlyn, for fifty-two years devoted owner of Clovelly.
Rubbing; 13×22; signed E.G. del. L.C. scp. December 1937.

705 Tablet in memory of SEYMOUR ASQUITH.
[This work was executed early in 1938 but it has not been possible to obtain more precise data.]

I

705A Portland headstone surmounted by a cross within foliage, St. John the Evangelist, Holdenhurst, Bournemouth, Hants, in memory of GERALD GRAHAM PEEL. Born 9 August 1878, died 16 October 1937.
Work executed *c.* 1937.

706 Tablet at Hatfield, Herts., in memory of WILLIAM GASCOYNE-CECIL, D.D., Bishop of Exeter second son of the 3rd Marquis of Salisbury, K.G.
Half full-size setting-out for inscription; 7×39; signed E.G. Pigotts, High Wycombe, 19.1.38.

706A Alphabet of incised 2 in. letters with Numerals.
Outline drawing; signed E.G. 19.1.38.

707 Headstone of Delabole slate in Bunhill Fields Burial Ground, London, in memory of Rev. WILLIAM HOOKE, 1601–1678. M.A. Trinity College, Oxford, 1623. Teacher of the First Church in New Haven, Connecticut, 1644–56. Chaplain to Oliver Cromwell & Master of the Savoy Hospital until the close of the Commonwealth. The tablet was erected by the New Haven Church through the generosity of a collateral descendant.
Work executed January 1938.

708 Recumbent tombstone of Portland stone in the private cemetery, Wilton House, Salisbury, in memory of MICHAEL GEORGE HERBERT, 1893–1932, son of Sir Michael Henry Herbert, P.C., G.C.M.G., C.B.
Pencil sketch by E.G., of Coat of Arms as redesigned for the tombstone; unsigned and undated.
Rubbing of inscription on face of gravestone ($2\frac{3}{4}$ in. letters); $12\frac{1}{4} \times 18$. On the same sheet are rubbings of the $1\frac{1}{2}$ in. letters which are incised round the sides of the stone; signed E.G. del., L.C., Sc. Feb. 1938.
Rubbing of shield; $18 \times 14\frac{3}{4}$; endorsed 'Sir Sydney Herbert. L.C. scp. & del. May '38'.

709 Headstone in memory of HENRY DAVID APPERLY, d. 30 July 1937.
Pencil drawing (coloured); signed E.G. 5.2.38.
Actual size 42×13 approx.

709A Head and footstone of Delabole slate, St. Stephen's, Lympne, Hythe, Kent, in memory of A. H. HALLAM MURRAY, 1854–1934.
Pencil drawing 1 in. scale (coloured); signed E.G. 30.8.37.
Rubbing of inscription; $24 \times 26\frac{1}{2}$; signed E.G. del., L.C. scp., April 1938.

710 Lectern in Hopton-Wood stone, in All Saints Church, Lusaka, N. Rhodesia, in memory of Lady YOUNG, wife of Sir Hubert Young.

This carries an inscription on the column (letters successively beneath one another): IF I TAKE THE WINGS OF THE MORNING EVEN THERE SHALL THY HAND LEAD ME . . .

Total height of Lectern 4 ft. 5 in. above floor line.

Pencil drawings and sketches; ⅛ f-s.; signed E.G. and given various dates in May and June, 1938.

711 An alphabet carved for a client [Grady] in the U.S.A. of *Sculpture and Memorials* London.

Work executed July 1938.

712 Inscription: PLAYHOUSE, in letters approx. 12 in. high on the New Repertory Theatre, Beaumont Street, Oxford.

Work executed August 1938.

713 Gravestone of Portland stone outside South Transept of Peterborough Cathedral in memory of EMILY JANE STOCKS, 1847–1937.

Work executed August 1938.

714 Ledgerstone of green Cumberland slate in Cloister Garden, Canterbury Cathedral, in memory of HUGH RICHARD LAWRIE SHEPPARD, 1880–1937.

Pencil drawing (coloured); signed E.G. 22.4.38.

Rubbing of inscription; 67 × 23¾; signed E.G. del. L.C. scp. Aug–Sept. 1938.

715 Portland headstone, surmounted by a cross, in Ladywell cemetery, Brockley, Kent, in memory of ALICE ANN JONES 1856–1937.

Pencil drawing, 1 in. scale; signed E.G. 10.8.38.

Rubbing of inscription; 15¼ × 17¼; endorsed by E.G. 'L.C. scp. & del. Oct. 1938'.

[This commemorates the mother of David Jones.]

716 Hopton-Wood stone tablet in memory of WALTER DOUGLAS WELLS. M.A. Cantab., 1889–1938, for 23 years a master at Chigwell School.

Rubbing of tablet; 9 × 26¾; endorsed by E.G. 'for A. Randall Wells. L.C. del. & scp. Sept., 1938'.

717 Headstone with kerbing in Aberdeen grey granite at Drumoak, Aberdeen, in memory of ROBERT WILLIAMS, Baronet, 1860–1938.

Pencil drawings for this and an alternative design; signed E.G. 26.9.38.

718 Delabole slate tablet in Zion Congregational Church, Coronation Road, Southville, Bristol, in memory of THOMAS SILCOX CLEVERDON, 1866–1937, and JANE LOUISA CLEVERDON, 1871–1937.
Scraper board draft; signed E.G. 28.2.36.
Rubbing of inscription; 10 × 13; signed E.G. del., L.C. scp. October 1938.

719 Tablet in Hampstead Cemetery in memory of JOHANNA GUTT-MANN, 1854–1938.
Half f-s. drawing of inscription; $2\frac{1}{2} \times 6\frac{1}{4}$; signed E.G. 3.10.38.

720 Hopton-Wood tablet in memory of MARY CONSTANCE WEMYSS, 1862–1937.
Beneath this inscription is the carving of a leaf with: VALE PAULISPER DILECTISSIMA.
Pencil sketch by E.G. unsigned and undated.
Rubbing of tablet; 13 × 24; endorsed by E.G. 'L.C. del & scp., Oct., 1938'. (See also No. 733A.)

721 Foundation stone of the Roman Catholic Church St. Peter the Apostle, Gorleston-on-Sea, Great Yarmouth. This church, designed by E.G., was consecrated in June 1939.
Drawing for inscription; 24 October 1938.

722 Recumbent gravestone, worked in York stone, in memory of NICO JUNGMAN, 1872–1935.
Pencil drawing; signed E.G. 10.10.38.
Rubbing; $38\frac{1}{2} \times 21\frac{3}{4}$; signed L.C. 1939.

723 Two oak panels with incised lettering in the Chapel, Rossall School, Fleetwood, Lancs., commemorating the gift by Old Rossallians of double windows in memory of LEONARD ROMNEY FURNEAUX, 1859–1934, a master of the school 1884–1920.
Drawing for inscription made 25 November 1938.

724 Portland headstone in memory of ESSIE A. HOLMES, 1860–1938.
Pencil drawing; signed E.G. 7.10.38.
Rubbing of inscription; $19 \times 13\frac{1}{4}$; signed Michael Richey, (& E.G.) del. M.R. scp., December, 1938.

725 Hopton-Wood stone tablet; letters incised: ΒΙΤΖΗΛΟΒΡΥΣΙΣ [Translation: VITZELOVRYSIS—The spring of Vitzelos] followed by elegiac couplet: ΩΖΕΙΝ ΕΥ ΜΕΝ ΠΙΝΕ, ΧΑΡΙΝΑ. ΕΧΕ . . .

Pen and ink sketch; signed E.G. 5.12.38. with a note: 'Tablet 19″ high ×
3′ 10″ (1″ letters)'.
This was commissioned by John Pendlebury, F.S.A., who, with others had
been completing the British School at Athens excavations at Kaphi in central
Crete. The tablet (since destroyed whether by occupying troops or by local
hooligans is uncertain) faced a drinking trough. The epigram, an adaptation by
Pendlebury of classical models, may be translated: 'O stranger, drink well,
and be grateful to those who built the fountain; our mouths, too, were dry.
A memento of the English archaeologists—1939'.

726 Slab of Cumberland slate in the crypt of Westminster Cathedral, London,
in memory of COMES ALEXANDER PHILIPPUS CONSTANTINUS
LUDOVICUS BENCKENDORFF, 1849–1917.
Pencil drawing; ⅛ full-size; endorsed 'letters incised, shield sunk in relief.
E.G. 10.10.38.'
Rubbing of inscription; 69 × 23¼; signed E,G. & L.C. April 1939.

727 Portrait panel of Hopton-Wood stone beneath which is an inscription in
memory of OTTOLINE MORRELL, 1873–1938.
Pencil drawing; signed E.G. 9.1.39.
Rubbing of inscription; 17½ × 20¾; signed E.G. del., L.C. scp. April, 1939.
[This work though executed was not erected, and is now in the possession of
Ottoline Morrell's daughter, Mrs. Julian Vinogradoff, 10 Gower St., London,
W.C.1.]
(See also No. 730.]

728 Portland head and kerb stones in the churchyard St. Botolph's, Farn-
borough, Banbury, in memory of STANLEY MOTTRAM RANKIN,
d. 1933, and of MARY, his wife, d. 1935.
Pencil drawing (coloured); signed E.G. 15.12.38.
Rubbing of inscription; 31 × 24½; signed E.G. del., Walter Ritchie, scp.
May, 1939.

729 Tablet of Hopton-Wood stone in St. Winifred's Church, Holbeck,
Worksop, Notts., in memory of Major Lord WILLIAM AUGUSTUS
CAVENDISH-BENTINCK, 1899–1902.
Pen and ink drawing (tinted); ⅛ full-size; signed E.G. 20.1.29.
Rubbing; 33½ × 19¾; endorsed 'L.C. Del. & Scp. H. W. Stone, May 1939'.

730 Recumbent tombstone of Hopton-Wood stone in St. Winifred's, Holbeck,
Worksop, Notts., in memory of OTTOLINE wife of Philip Morrell and

sister of the sixth Duke of Portland, K.G., who died April 21, 1938 in her sixty-fifth year.

Actual size 68⅝ × 28.

Pencil drawing (coloured); signed E.G. 6.2.39.

F-s. detail; signed E.G. 1.6.39.

(See also No. 727.)

731 Stations of the Cross, worked in Hopton-Wood stone, St. Alban's, Charles Street, Oxford.

Rubbings, of the individual stations; 17¾ × 14¾; signed E.G. del., L.C. scp. June 1939.

Work executed 1939–40.

732 Raised table-stone of Portland in Blakeney Churchyard, Holt, Norfolk, in memory of KENNETH EDGAR MYLNE BARKER. Also of Anna-bella Catherine his wife.

Pencil drawing (coloured); signed and dated E.G. 23.6.39.

Actual size about 72 × 33.

732A Alphabet, the letters of roman caps and lower-case together with arabic numerals, incised and coloured. Carved on Hopton-Wood stone with (above) text from Virgil, 'Felix qui potuit' and (at foot) 'rerum cognoscare cauaas', in italic letters and 'signed' '1939 E.G.'

Rubbing of alphabet only; 22 × 17½; signed E.G. del. and scp. June 1939 (for Graham Carey).

[This is one of the few inscriptional works E.G. 'signed'.]   [*See Plate XVI*]

732B An alphabet of Roman and lower-case letters, together with numerals, incised and coloured, on Hopton-Wood stone. For *Sculpture and Memorials* London.

Rubbing; 17½ × 23½; endorsed 'H. W. Stone L.C. del et scp. Spring 1939 for S. & M.'

732C An alphabet of Roman and lower-case letters, together with numerals, incised and coloured, on Hopton-Wood stone. For *Sculpture and Memorials* London.

Rubbing; 23 × 17½; endorsed 'E.G. and Walter Ritchie del. Walter Ritchie scp. Spring 1939.'

732D An alphabet of Roman and lower-case letters, together with numerals, incised and coloured, on Hopton-Wood stone. For *Sculpture and Memorials* London.

Rubbing; $18\frac{1}{4} \times 23\frac{3}{4}$; endorsed 'H. W. Stone. E.G., del. Michael Richey scp. Spring 1939 for S. & M.'

733 Carving in Portland stone at Lodge Hill Farm, Coombe Hill, Wendover, Bucks., the residence of E. A. Randag, depicting St. Hubert and stag. This is surmounted by a crucifix and an inscription reading: EGO SUM JESUS QUEM PERSEQUERIS.
Pencil drawing (tinted); signed E.G. 17.6.39.
[In his diary, under 25 Sept., 1940, E.G. records having worked on this carving *in situ* all that afternoon. An entry the following day records having finished it. This appears to have been his last stone carving.]

733A Raised ledgerstone of Portland stone with inscriptions on each side and on each end, in the churchyard, Didbrook Church, Stanway, Glos., in memory of MARY wife of Hugo Tenth Earl of Wemyss, 1862–1937.
Pencil drawing in perspective; signed E.G. 27.7.39.
(See also No. 720.)

734 Head and footstones of Hopton-Wood stone in Norwich in memory of GEOFFREY COLMAN, 1892–1935.
There are a pencil sketch and no less than five careful drawings of different designs. Two of the latter are signed E.G. 8.12.38., two are unsigned and the fifth (the accepted design), 1 in. scale, is signed E.G. 19.3.39.
Rubbing of inscription; $30\frac{1}{4} \times 21$; signed E.G. del. L.C. scp. July 1939.

734A Tablet of Delabole slate intended for No. 25 Soho Square commemorating THOMAS BARNES 1785–1841 (Editor of *The Times* 1817–1841) who lived there.
Rubbing; $15 \times 24\frac{3}{4}$; signed E.G. del. & scp., June 1939.
[This tablet was not erected; it is now in the hands of The Times Publishing Company.]
(See also No. 671.)

735 Celtic cross of green Hornton stone at Knockdolian, Ayrshire, in memory of HENRY WILSON McCONNEL, M.A., M.B. (Cantab.), M.R.C.S. (Eng.).
Pencil drawing (tinted); signed E.G. 3.4.39.
Rubbing of inscription; $17\frac{3}{4} \times 7\frac{1}{4}$; signed E.G. del., L.C. scp. July 1939.

736 Tablets of Roman stone on Peek, Frean & Company's Sports Pavilion, Sidcup Road, Lee, Kent.

There are two tablets and a clock face, viz.

(a) Tablet recording the gift of the pavilion by the President of the Club, Philip Carr, 1939.

Rubbing of tablet; 11¾ × 51¼.

(b) Tablet lettered; AND WHEN THE ONE GREAT SCORER COMES TO WRITE AGAINST YOUR NAME—HE MARKS NOT THAT YOU WON OR LOST BUT HOW YOU PLAYED THE GAME. (From *Alumnus Football* by Grantland Rice.)

Rubbing of tablet; 12 × 77¼.

(c) Clock face in arabic figures 1 to 12.

Rubbing; 16 in. in diameter.

All the above rubbings are signed E.G. del., L.C. scp. August 1939.

737 Head and footstones in Chelsfield Churchyard, Kent, in memory of CHARLES RONALD VAWDREY COUTTS, 1876–1938.

Pencil drawing; signed E.G. 3.4.39.

Rubbing; 33 × 28½; endorsed by E.G., L.C. del. and scp. August, 1939.

738 Headstone in memory of MARY LETITIA OGSTON wife of Sir Herbert GRIERSON, 1868–1937.

Pencil sketch for 2½ in. roman caps; signed E.G. 10.9.39.

Actual size; approx. 30 × 41.

739 Headstone of Delabole slate in memory of PERCY WALTER WHITE, 1874–1938, in the churchyard St. Genesius, St. Gennys, Bude, N. Cornwall.

Rubbing of inscription; 24¾ × 18½; signed E.G. del., L.C. scp., Oct. 1939.

740 Foundation stone, incorporating Coat of Arms, for Nottingham County Hall, laid by the Duke of Portland, 21 November, 1939.

Pencil drawing; ¼ f-s.; 12½ × 9; signed E.G. 30.10.39.

741 Tablet of Delabole slate in Memorial Chapel, Rockingham Castle, Market Harborough, in memory of LAVINIA, wife of BARON von ROEDER, 1853–1933.

Pen and ink drawing; ⅛ f-s.; signed E.G. 1.5.39.

Rubbing of tablet; 13 × 19¾; signed E.G. del., L.C. scp. Oct.–Dec. 1939.

742 Headstone in memory of EDWARD ORFORD CAPON, d. 1939, aged 65.

Pencil drawing; signed E.G. October 1939.

743 Portland head and footstone in the cemetery Wellington, Somerset, in memory of JOHN WESLEY CLIFT, 1858–1939.
Pencil drawing; signed E.G. 11.11.39.
Actual size; 42 × 30; letters 1½ in. high.

744 Portland headstone on plinth with Coat of Arms in relief, and kerbing, in Horson Cemetery, Torpoint, Plymouth, in memory of EVA MARGARET SANDEMAN.
The work was executed in 1942 by David Kindersley from drawings made by Eric Gill in January 1940.

745 Oak panel with badges and inscription (both coloured) on west wall of the Chapel, Blundell's School, Tiverton, in memory of HUGH LEWIS OWEN, 1882–1938.
Size of panel 12 × 15.
Work executed in 1940.

746 Recumbent gravestone of Portland stone in Newick churchyard, Sussex, in memory of GERALD MORLEY HORDER, 1878–1939.
Pencil drawing, in perspective; signed E.G. 1.1.40.

747 Tablet of Hopton-Wood stone, on a wall immediately opposite Trout Inn, Godstow, Oxford, commemorating acquisition of land by the Oxford Preservation Trust, in 1934, through a gift by Philip Leslie Agnew, in memory of his son EWAN SIEGFRIED AGNEW, a student at New College, Oxford, 1912–1914.
Pen and ink sketch; 1 in. scale; signed E.G. 3.8.39.
Rubbing; signed E.G. del., L.C. scp. Jan. 1940.
Actual size of tablet 18¾ × 30¾.

748 Portland head and curb stones in Ewhurst Churchyard, Surrey, in memory of PAUL LAUDER, 1880–1939.
Pencil drawing, in perspective; signed E.G. 15.2.40.

748A Table-stone paperweight with inscription: THE SOULS OF THE RIGHTEOUS ARE IN THE HAND OF GOD & THERE SHALL NO TORMENT TOUCH THEM.
Rubbing; 3¾ × 2¼; signed E.G., scp. April 1940.
[This was commissioned by Wilma Lady Cawdor.]

749 Ledgerstone in East Sheen cemetery, Mortlake, London, S.W.14, in memory of CHARLES FREDERICK KEARLEY.
Work executed 1940.

750 Gravestone of Blue Hornton stone in the garden of Baroda House, Kensington Palace Gardens, inscribed: 'HEATHER My constant companion and friend. Beloved by all. B. July 30th 1928, D. Feby. 26th 1940.' This was commissioned by Sir Sydney Cockerell, on behalf of Mrs. Chester Beatty, for a little dog.
Scraperboard drawing; approx $\frac{1}{12}$ f-s.; signed E.G. 17.3.40.
Rubbing; $21\frac{3}{4} \times 30\frac{1}{2}$; signed E.G. del., L.C. scp. June 1940.

751 Cruciform headstone of Portland stone at Box, nr. Chippenham, Wilts., in memory of PATRICIA MARY LEVINGE, d. January 1940, aged 5 months.
Pencil drawing (tinted); signed E.G. 27.2.40.
Rubbing of inscription; 15×15; endorsed by E.G. 'L.C. del. & scp. June 1940.'

752 Portland ledgerstone in Stonefall Cemetery, Harrogate, in memory of TERESA MARY KELLY, d. 1938.
Rubbing of portion of inscription; $24\frac{1}{2} \times 20\frac{1}{4}$; endorsed by E.G. 'L.C. del. & scp. August 1940.'

753 Ledgerstone of Blue Hornton stone, inscription in incised Roman capitals, in churchyard St. Lawrence, South Hinksey, Oxon., in memory of DAVID DUNCAN BADEN-POWELL, d. 7 Sept 1939.
Pencil drawing (coloured); signed E.G. 4.6.40.
Rubbing of inscription; $54\frac{3}{4} \times 20\frac{1}{4}$; signed E.G. & D.T. del., D.T. scp. Aug.–Sept. 1940.

754 Tablet of Portland stone on a wall in the garden of Sir Winston Churchill's house Chartwell, Westerham, Kent. This records: THE GREATER PART OF THIS WALL WAS BUILT BETWEEN THE YEARS 1925 & 1932 BY WINSTON WITH HIS OWN HANDS. This was commissioned by Lady Churchill.
Rubbing of inscription; 30×18; signed L.C[ribb]. & E.G. del., L.C. scp. Aug. 1940.
(See also No. 754A.)

754A Inscription on sundial in the garden of Sir Winston Churchill's house, Chartwell, Westerham, Kent, commissioned by Lady Churchill. The inscription runs:

HERE LIES THE BALI DOVE.
IT DOES NOT DO TO WANDER
TOO FAR FROM SOBER MEN,
BUT THERE'S AN ISLAND YONDER—
I THINK OF IT AGAIN

August 1940.
(See also No. 754.)

755 Headstone of Hopton-Wood stone, in Daviot Churchyard, Inverness-shire, in memory of VINCENT CARTWRIGHT VICKERS, 1878–1939. Rubbing of inscription; $22 \times 13\frac{1}{2}$; signed L.C. del. & scp. May 1940.
[This commemorates the father of Wilma, Lady Cawdor.]

755A Headstone of Hopton-Wood stone, in Daviot Churchyard, Inverness-shire, in memory of ANTONY ALBERT VICKERS 1913–1939, elder son of Vincent Cartwright Vickers.
Rubbing of inscription; 28×13; signed L.C. del. & scp. May 1940.
[This commemorates a half brother of Wilma, Lady Cawdor.]

756 Hornton Stone headstone in Apperley churchyard, Glos., in memory of ALGERNON WALTER STRICKLAND, 1891–1939.
Pencil drawing in perspective; signed E.G. 23.8.40.

757 Hopton-Wood stone tablet, St. Peter's, Dumbleton, Evesham, in memory of COLLINS ASHWIN, Rector of Dumbleton, 1904–1938.
Pencil sketch; $\frac{1}{4}$ full-size; signed E.G. 19.9.40.
Rubbing of inscription; $16\frac{1}{4} \times 16\frac{3}{4}$; signed L.C. & E.G. del., L.C. scp. Sept. 1940.

758 Portland head and footstones in Leamington Cemetery in memory of EDITH EIRENE CHAMBERS, 1865–1940.
Pencil drawing; signed E.G. 29.3.40. and another; $\frac{1}{8}$ full-size; signed EG. 16.10.40.

759 Gravetone, St. Mary and St. John Baptist, Newtown, Newbury, Berks., in memory of SYBIL MARY WENTWORTH ROSKILL, 1871–1931, and of JOHN ROSKILL, 1860–1940.
E.G.'s work (of 145 letters), carved by Laurie Cribb, was done on an existing stone. A note in his diary under 13th October, 1940, reads: 'Enthoven [the

architect] inscription sketch in afternoon.' This was the last entry he made in his diary prior to entering Harefield Hospital, whither he went November 1st, and where he died November 17th 1940.

760 Headstone at Alnwick, Northumberland, in memory of LYDIA KATE ARMSTRONG, 1867–1940.
A pencil drawing (coloured) signed E.G. 29.10.40. appears to be the last drawing E.G. made for inscriptional work. He was admitted to Harefield Hospital, 1 Nov. 1940 and died there on the 17th of that month.

761 Crucifixion. A carving on sycamore wood with incised inscription: ET ANTE QVAM ME IN VOCETIS, DI CAM: ECCE ADSVM.
This carving ($11\frac{1}{2} \times 8$) was incised by Denis Tegetmeier after a drawing by E.G., 18 October 1940.
It is now in the collection of S. Samuels, Liverpool.

762 Head and footstones in the communal cemetery, Speen, Bucks., in memory of Eric Gill, born 22 Feb. 1882, died 17 Nov. 1940. The inscription, surmounted by a cross, reads: PRAY FOR ME / ERIC GILL / STONE CARVER / 1882–1940. Carved on the footstone is the device *St. Thomas Hand's* and *Veritas* which E.G. used as an identifying symbol in many of the books he wrote.
Rubbing of inscription on headstone; $15\frac{1}{2} \times 19$.
Rubbing of carving on footstone; $8\frac{1}{2} \times 7$.
This inscription, designed by E.G. himself, was cut by his assistant Laurie Cribb.

Two other memorials may here be recorded. The earlier one is a tablet (drawing; 9×12) let into the floor beneath the XIVth Station of the Cross in Westminster Cathedral, letters incised: E.G. / LAPIDARIUS / 1882–1940 / R.I.P. This was designed and cut by Laurie Cribb in 1942.
The later one is a tablet in Portland stone (rubbing; $21\frac{1}{4} \times 19\frac{1}{2}$) affixed to the wall of 32 Hamilton Road, Brighton. The inscription, which is surmounted by a carving, in relief, of dolphins, reads: ERIC GILL / STONE CARVER / WAS BORN IN THIS / HOUSE ON THE 22nd / FEBRUARY 1882 / *Erected by the Regency Society*. This was drawn and cut by Joseph Cribb and fixed in September 1960. The design follows that which E.G. himself drew for similar tablets affixed to houses in Brighton. (Cf. No. 458.)
It is altogether fitting that these memorials should have been worked by the brothers Cribb who were E.G.'s assistants throughout the best part of his working life as a stone carver.

BIBLIOGRAPHY

Art of Lettering, The. Report of a Special Committee of the British Institute of Industrial Art. Oxford: University Press, 1931. Contains references to E.G. and illustrations of five of his works.

BEAUJON, PAUL (Beatrice Warde)

'Eric Gill: Sculptor of Letters.' *The Fleuron*, No. VII, pp. 27–51. Cambridge: University Press, 1930. Contains two collotype reproductions of inscriptions: John Sargent (cf. No. 469) and Sir Frederick Bridge (cf. No. 461).

BENSON, JOHN HOWARD and CAREY, ARTHUR GRAHAM

Elements of Lettering, The. Newport, R.I.: John Stevens, 1940. Contains reference to E.G. and a reproduction (Plate XXVII) of an alphabet cut by him (cf. No. 732A).

GILL, ERIC

Autobiography. London: Jonathan Cape. 1940.

'Inscriptions.' *The Burlington Magazine*, Vol. XVI, No. LXXXIV, March 1910, pp. 318–28. Illustrated.

'Stone Carving.' A contribution to *The Encyclopædia Britannica*, 14th ed., 1929. Vol. 21, pp. 437–8. London: The Encyclopædia Britannica Co.

HARLING, ROBERT

'Early Alphabets of Eric Gill, The.' *Alphabet and Image*, No. 3, December 1946, pp. 61–67. With three folding reproductions of lettering.

'Experiments and Alphabets.' *The Penrose Annual*, Vol. XXXVIII, 1936, pp. 60–64. London: Lund, Humphries, Ltd. With illustrations.

Hopton-Wood Stone. A Book for the Architect and Craftsman. London: Hopton-Wood Stone Firms, Limited, 1947.

JOHNSTON, EDWARD

Manuscript & Inscription Letters for Schools & Classes & for the use of Craftsmen. Portfolio with sixteen plates, five of which are of the work of E.G. London: Sir Isaac Pitman & Sons Ltd. Ninth impression, 1950. Plates 13 and 14 are also obtainable as Lettering Sheets Nos. 1 and 2 respectively of the four sheets published as *Reproductions of Lettering by Eric Gill* (q.v. infra).

Writing and Illuminating and Lettering. London: Sir Isaac Pitman & Sons Ltd. With a chapter 'Inscriptions in Stone' by E.G. Contains a collotype reproduction (Plate XXIV) of the inscription GLORIA IN ALTISSIMIS DEO . . . (cf. No. 22) with a descriptive note (pp. 486–7) also portion of an inscription (cf. No. 57) in Brasenose College, Oxford (Fig. 208).

KEHR, WOLFGANG

Eric Gill als Schriftkunstler. Frankfurt am Main: Börsenblatt für den Deutschen Buchhandel, 17 Jahrgang Nr. 77a, 28 September 1961, pp. 1543–1926. A copiously illustrated and detailed survey of E.G.'s lettering. This includes drawn, incised and engraved lettering as well as a complete record of his type faces. A full bibliography is provided.

Picture Book of Roman Alphabets, A. London: Victoria & Albert Museum, 1933. Contains repro-ductions (pp. 20–23) of an alphabet cut by E.G. (cf. No. 498). This was cut in 1927; the original is exhibited in the Department of Architecture and Sculpture in the Museum.

READ, HERBERT

'Aesthetics of Tombstones, The.' *The Listener*, 2 May 1934, pp. 738–40. London: British Broadcasting Corporation. Contains a reference to E.G. and a photograph of one of his works.

Reproductions of Lettering by Eric Gill. London: Victoria & Albert Museum, 1936. These are four Lettering Sheets the first two of which are f.-s. collotype reproductions of Plates 13 and 14 of Edward Johnston's *Manuscript & Inscription Letters* (q.v. supra). The third is of the panel EX DIVINA PVLCHRITVDINE . . . (cf. No. 479A also Nos. 168A, 168B and 479.)

Roman Lettering. A book of Alphabets and Inscriptions. London: Victoria and Albert Museum, and H.M.S.O., 1958. This is in effect a revised edition of *A Picture Book of Roman Alphabets q.v.* (*ante*) and is No. 12 of the series of Large Picture Books. Plate 7 reproduces the two Alphabets cut by E.G. in 1909 not in 1925 as stated (cf. Nos. 168A and 168B.)

Sculptured Memorials & Headstones. London: Sculptured Memorials, Ebury Street, S.W.1. The 2nd edition (1937) contains fourteen illustrations of E.G.'s work. The 3rd edition (1938) contains nine of the illustrations of the 2nd edition and an additional one (cf. Nos. 668–9).

SHEWRING, Walter (ed.)

Letters of Eric Gill. London: Jonathan Cape, 1947.

WARDE, BEATRICE

A Keepsake for the Guests at the opening on October 14th 1958 of an Exhibition of the work of Eric Gill, Master of Lettering held at Monotype House, under the auspices of The Monotype Corporation Limited. London: The Monotype Corporation Limited, 1958. With numerous illustrations of work exhibited.

'Eric Gill: Master of Lettering.' *The Monotype Recorder*, Vol. 41, No. 3, 1958. The whole number commemorates the Exhibition opened 14 October (q.v. the *Keepsake* supra). Contains nine illustrations of lettering for inscriptions.

Monotype News Letter 56. December 1958. Contains a report of the Exhibition of 14 October together with a four-page inset reproducing outstanding items of drawings, carvings and rubbings, etc.

INDEX OF PERSONS AND INSTITUTIONS

Capitals denote persons commemorated.

Names in lower-case type relate to persons, or institutions who
either commissioned the work or have it in their keeping.

K

INDEX OF LOCATIONS

INDEX OF QUOTATIONS

ALPHABETS

THE PLATES

PLATE I   Rubbing of Gill's first letter-cutting on stone, *c.* 1901
(No. 1)

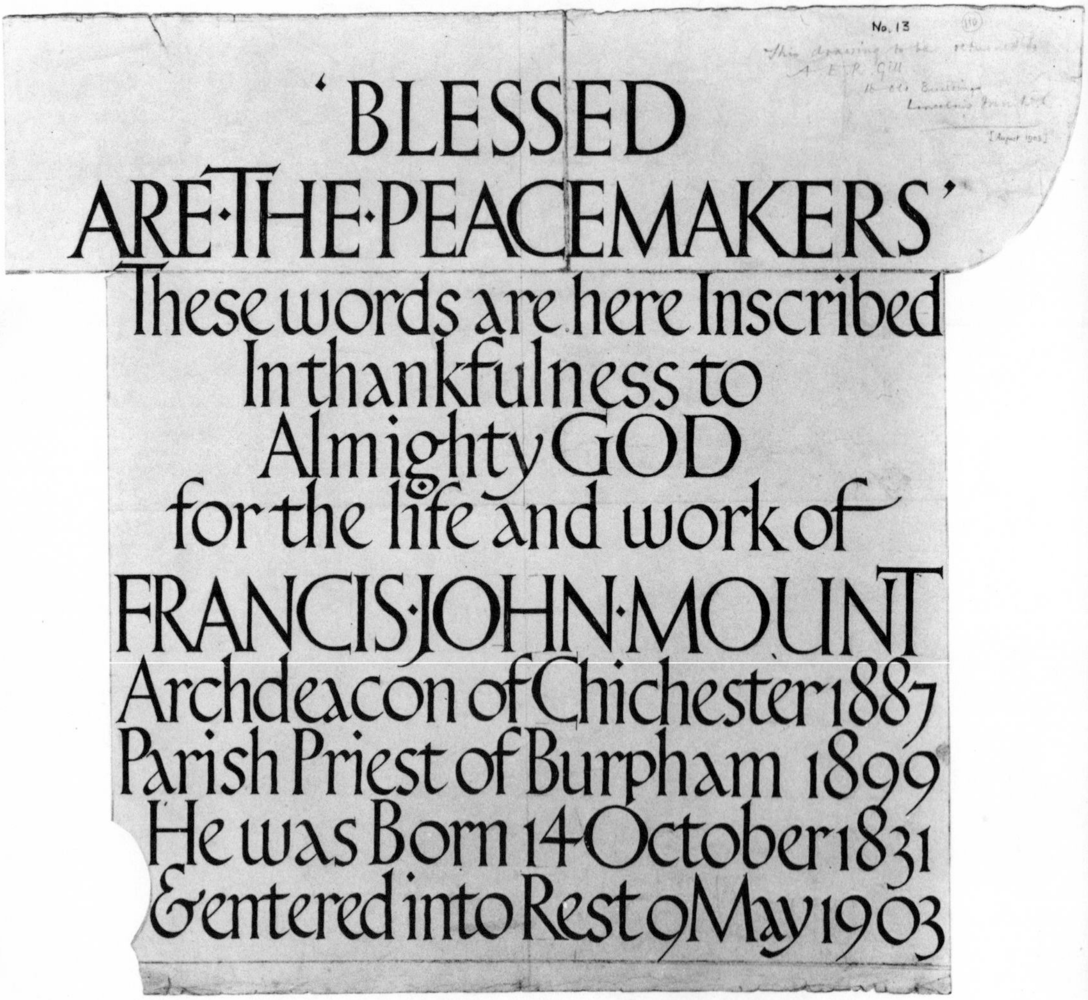

'BLESSED
ARE·THE·PEACEMAKERS'
These words are here Inscribed
In thankfulness to
Almighty GOD
for the life and work of
FRANCIS·JOHN·MOUNT
Archdeacon of Chichester 1887
Parish Priest of Burpham 1899
He was Born 14 October 1831
& entered into Rest 9 May 1903

PLATE II   Drawing for an epitaph, 1903
(No. 13)

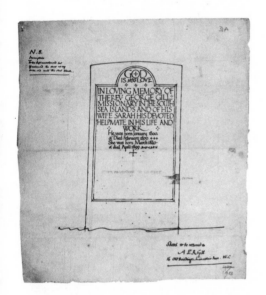

PLATE III   Rubbing of part of a tombstone, with two sketches, 1903
(No. 20)

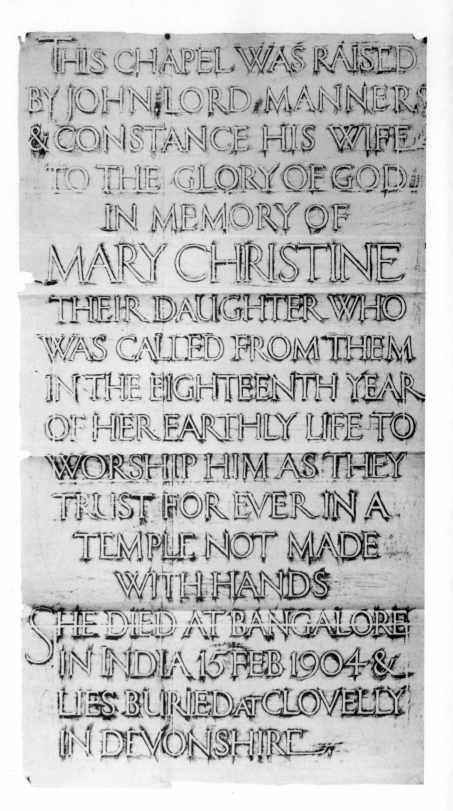

PLATE IV   Rubbing of an inscription, 1906
(No. 97)

In memory of
GENERAL SIR HENRY
AUGUSTUS SMYTH
K · C · M · G
Colonel Commandant Royal
Artillery, & sometime Governor
& Commander-in-chief of Malta.
Son of Admiral W. H. Smyth
R.N. K.S.F. D.C.L.
He devoted over 50 years of his
life to the service of his country
& died at St. John's Lodge, Stone,
18 Oct. 1906. Aged 80.
Believing in the everlasting
goodness of God.
✝

18 Sept. 1

PLATE V   Rubbing of a stone tablet, 1907
(No. 110)

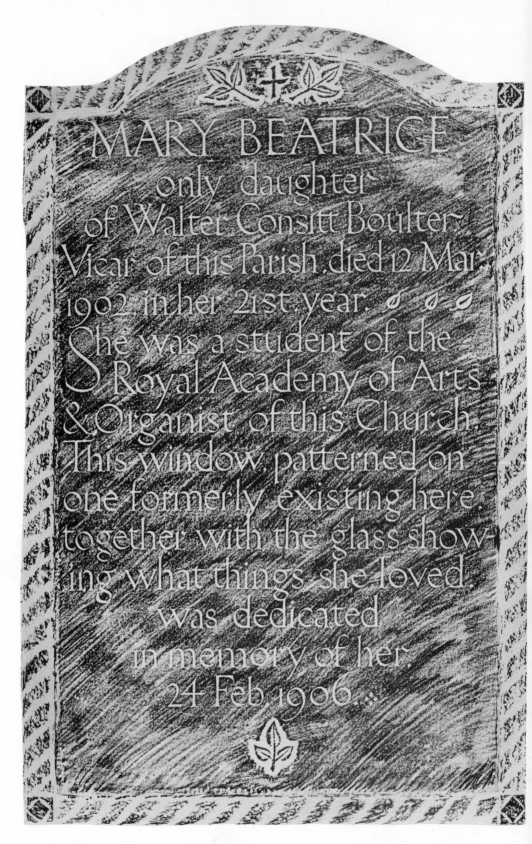

MARY BEATRICE
only daughter
of Walter Consitt Boulter
Vicar of this Parish died 12 Mar
1902 in her 21st year.
She was a student of the
Royal Academy of Arts
& Organist of this Church.
This window, patterned on
one formerly existing here
together with the glass showing what things she loved,
was dedicated
in memory of her
24 Feb 1906.

PLATE VI   Rubbing of a marble tablet, 1908
(No. 154)

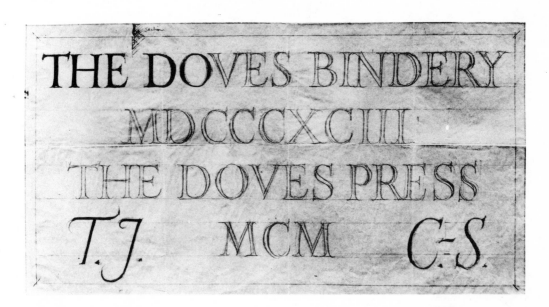

PLATE VII Sketch and rubbing of a tablet, 1910
(No. 211)

DIEU ET MON DROIT

THE LORD RICHARD
WELLESLEY
CAPTAIN OF
No. 3 COMPANY
1st. BATTALION
GRENADIER GUARDS
2nd. SON OF ARTHUR,
FOURTH DUKE OF
WELLINGTON
BORN 30 SEPT. 1879
KILLED 29 OCT. 1914
AT YPRES, BELGIUM
FIGHTING THE GERMANS
IN THE GREAT WAR
HIS WIDOW
SET THIS STONE HERE
IN HIS MEMORY

PLATE VIII   First design for tablet shown opposite, 1916
(No. 314)

PLATE IX   Rubbing of tablet in Hopton-Wood stone, 1916
(No. 314)

Gradu Div... ...erso Via Una

BRIGADIER GENERAL
JOHN EDMOND GOUGH
V.C. C.B. C.M.G.
A.D.C. to H.M. the King,
of the Rifle Brigade.
Chief of the Staff of the First Army
British Expeditionary Force

PLATE X   Drawing of coat of arms and part of inscription, 1921
(No. 372)

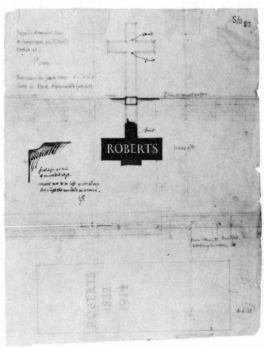

PLATE XI   Coloured pencil drawing, 1920, with an alternative
pen and ink design, 1921
(No. 382)

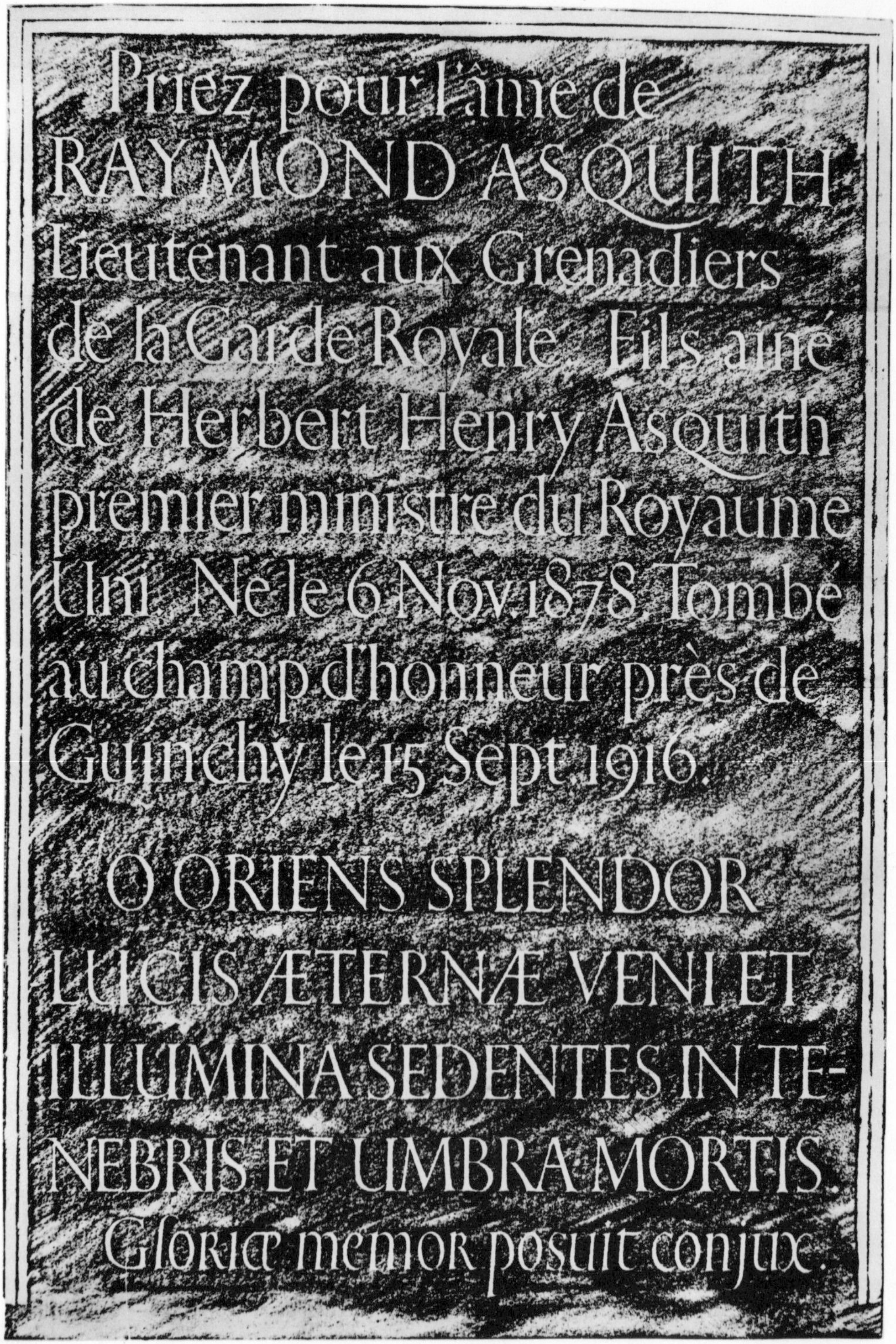

Priez pour l'âme de
RAYMOND ASQUITH
Lieutenant aux Grenadiers
de la Garde Royale Fils aîné
de Herbert Henry Asquith
premier ministre du Royaume
Uni Né le 6 Nov 1878 Tombé
au champ d'honneur près de
Guinchy le 15 Sept 1916.

O ORIENS SPLENDOR
LUCIS ÆTERNÆ VENI ET
ILLUMINA SEDENTES IN TE-
NEBRIS ET UMBRA MORTIS.
Gloriæ memor posuit conjux.

PLATE XII   Rubbing of stone tablet, 1922
(No. 414)

✠

TO THE GLORY OF GOD
AND IN MEMORY OF
WALTER HINES PAGE
1855 – 1918
AMBASSADOR
OF THE UNITED STATES
OF AMERICA TO THE
COURT OF ST JAMES'S
1913 – 1918
The friend of Britain in her
sorest need.

PLATE XIII   Rubbing of a marble tablet, 1923
(No. 427)

PLATE XIV   Fascia board, 1926 (since destroyed), in letters
later developed as Gill Sans
(No. 484)

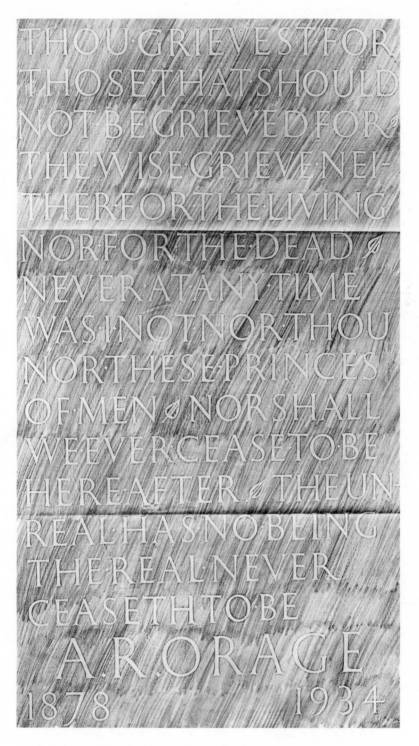

PLATE XV   Rubbing of a recumbent gravestone, 1935
(No. 635)

Felix qui potuit

A B C
D E F G H I J K
a b c d e f g h i j k l m n
L M N O P Q R
o p q r s t u v w x y z
S T U V W X Y
1 2 3 4 5 6 7 8 9 &
Z

rerum cognoscere causas. 1939 89

PLATE XVI Signed alphabet cut for Graham Carey, 1939
(No. 732A)